This is a pure [illegible] but there
is no biography The [illegible] [clas]s-
ified as wholely.

EINSTEIN, PROFILE OF THE MAN

EINSTEIN,

PROFILE OF THE MAN

BY PETER MICHELMORE

DODD, MEAD & COMPANY, NEW YORK

FOR V. J. AND B. J. MICHELMORE

AUTHOR'S NOTE

In February, 1962, I spent two days with Hans Albert Einstein in his home overlooking San Francisco Bay. Hans Albert, fifty-seven, the older son of Albert Einstein, is professor of hydraulic engineering at the University of California in Berkeley. He had never discussed his father before with any writer, at least not in depth. But he answered all my questions, and waited while I wrote down the answers. He did not ask to check my notes, or edit my book. He trusted me. It was the sort of naïvete his father had. Thank God for all naïve people, and I use the word in its noblest sense.

So, in acknowledging the sources for this profile, I thank Hans Albert Einstein first. He brought his father out of the shadows, enabling me to write the first frank portrait of Albert Einstein, the man. I also thank Otto Nathan and Helen Dukas, co-executors of the Estate of Albert Einstein, for answering countless questions, and I thank the Estate for permission to quote from Einstein's books, *Ideas and Opinions,* Crown

(1954); *Out of My Later Years,* New York Philosophical Library (1950); *The World As I See It,* Covici, Friede (1934). I acknowledge permission to quote from Einstein's diaries and letters as they appear in *Einstein on Peace,* Edited by Otto Nathan and Heinz Norden, Simon and Schuster (1960), Copyright, Estate of Albert Einstein.

Of the ten books I studied on Relativity, I found *The Universe and Dr. Einstein,* Lincoln Barnett, William Sloane Associates (1948), the most helpful.

Other books consulted in the preparation of this profile include: *Einstein, His Life and Times,* Philipp Frank, A. A. Knopf (1947); *Albert Einstein, Philosopher-Scientist,* edited by Paul Arthur Schilpp, Library of Living Philosophers (1949); *Einstein, An Intimate Study of a Great Man,* Dmitri Marianoff with Palma Wayne, Doubleday, Doran (1944); *Albert Einstein,* David Reichinstein, Stella Publishing House (1934); *Albert Einstein,* Anton Reiser, A.&C. Boni (1930); *Einstein, a Biography,* Antonina Vallentin, Weidenfeld & Nicolson (1954); *Quest,* Leopold Infeld, Doubleday, Doran (1941); *Abraham Flexner, an Autobiography,* Abraham Flexner, Simon and Schuster (1960); *Glimpses of the Great,* George Sylvester Viereck, The Macaulay Company (1930); *Helle Zeit-Dunkle Zeit,* edited by Carl Seelig, Europa Verlag (1956).

Acknowledgments to newspapers and magazines are made in the text, but I particularly want to express my gratitude to *The New York Times* for "morgue" facilities, and to *Nature* magazine (Macmillan Co. Ltd.) And my special thanks to Rada and Mirel Bercovici, literary executrices for the Estate of Konrad Bercovici, for permission to quote from Mr. Bercovici's interview with Einstein in Geneva in 1932.

Those who contributed most by letter or in interviews were Manfred Clynes, Harlow Shapley, Ernst Straus, Valentin Bargmann, Nathan Rosen, Norman S. Muller, Gracie Schwarz, Alexander Sachs, Fred Biallas, Frida Bucky.

My deep gratitude to Garry Barker and Herb Stauning, who gave me quiet places to work, and to Richard Lawrence, who went far beyond the call of friendship to translate tens of thousands of words of German into English.

While I wrote my book, my wife, Nanette, worked secretly on a bust of Albert Einstein. She did it in green clay on the top of a Seven-Up bottle. My two-year-old son called him "the Soda Man." I got the Soda Man, mounted and polished, as a gift when the book was done. Since my wife had already produced a daughter during the season, I thought it was a pretty nice thing to do.

P. M.

Weehawken, New Jersey
April, 1962

CONTENTS

CONTENTS

EINSTEIN, PROFILE OF THE MAN

CHAPTER 1

IVORY TOWER, IVORY MAN

The iron door opened into a narrow garret with a clean board floor and walls that had once been whitewashed. Wooden shelves against one wall were filled with letters, printed and typed papers, and soft-covered journals. There were no books. The other long wall was bare except for a small metal etching of Sir Isaac Newton. Two ladderback chairs with straw seats stood near this wall. At the end of the room, opposite the door, there was a sloping window, shut tight and splattered with grimy snow. It cast a pale light on a man who sat at a round parlor table.

This was Albert Einstein, aged forty. He was a theoretical physicist—some scientists said the best since Newton. But to the world at large, he was unknown. He was busy with pencil and paper, puzzling over mathematical equations. Frequently he paused in his work, inclining his head on the left side and twirling a strand of gray-black hair around and around his forefinger. His thumb came in lightly to keep the hair in place against his finger at the bottom of every turn. He got a tight twist before he sat upright and made more letters and numbers. Sometimes, instead of twirling his hair, he reached for one of the three pipes on his table and held the stem between his teeth. The pipes were dead, but much used and very stained.

His face, according to the light from the window, was a soiled ivory color. It was mostly smooth, but well creased around the eyes and stubbled at the jaw. His mass of dark, frizzled hair was streaked with white. His eyebrows arched upwards over dark brown eyes focused on infinity. The eyes gave pause. "Angel eyes," a friend had called them. Altogether, it was a handsome face.

Above the table, his stocky torso was covered by a cracked leather jacket. Below the table, a pair of brown trousers ended at the ankles, and there was an inch of white skin to felt bedroom slippers that were crushed down at the heel.

Einstein was immersed in his soaring, creative world of physics and had lost all sense of time. His attic was at the top of a building, a seven-story apartment house on Haberlandstrasse. The building was part of a city, haggard Berlin in the bitter autumn of 1919. But all that was outside the door. Inside, it was dim and silent and Einstein sat there in joyous solitary confinement.

He was trying to get to the truth about the universe—how and why it operated as it did. He was so caught up in abstract thought that it was hard for him to pay attention to what was happening on earth. When he did, he was disgusted by the pettiness and brutality of the world. He plunged back into his physics. "How I wish that somewhere there existed an island for those who are wise and of good will," he had written a friend. There was no island, so Einstein escaped to his attic.

He had locked his door on the ugliness of the earthly scene that morning of November 7, 1919.

The rest of Berlin had awakened to another day of thin porridge and thin hope. It was as miserable as any war day. Berlin again was like a beleaguered city, for Gustav Noske, German defense minister and virtual ruler of Berlin, had halted all public transport. Passenger trains were confiscated to carry coal and potatoes to areas where hunger and cold were killing people by the score. Buses were stopped to conserve fuel. Benzine was so scarce that few aircraft could be put into service. These were the reasons Noske gave for his declaration of a state of emergency, and they were real enough.

But there was another, more sinister, reason. November 7 was the second anniversary of the Bolshevik Revolution in Russia and Communist Party agents all over the world had in their hands a secret manifesto saying that this was the day when workers should be incited to overthrow governments, assassinate public officials, bomb army barracks and establish dictatorships of the proletariat. Berlin was a prime target. The amateur republican government of former basketmakers and blacksmiths was in daily danger of collapse under pressure from both extreme left and extreme right.

Noske, ruthless and cunning, was the government's strong man. And he knew about the Communist manifesto. By grabbing all transport, he prevented the Red uprising in Berlin. Communist rabble rousers could not get to the capital from their various posts around Germany. The Bolshevik demonstration had been planned for Wilhelmstrasse. To make doubly sure that nothing would happen, Noske's troops strung barbed wire across its approaches and then patrolled the barriers with loaded guns.

Berlin seemed the distress station of mankind that morning . . . barbed wire across snow-covered streets, new-born babies dying in unheated hospital wards, returned soldiers in tattered uniforms selling cigarettes on Unter den Linden, ghostly silence on Friedrichstrasse, factories shuttered, gaunt families hungrily sharing a stale loaf of black bread.

Gloom pervaded the suburban middle-class homes and apartments like a damp mist. The people had potatoes bought on the black market, margarine, skimmed milk, and—perhaps —sausage. There were small piles of coal in the cellars. But there was no real warmth, no fatness, no laughter.

Haberlandstrasse, where the Einstein family lived, was in such an area, hard to the city. The Einsteins were little known to their neighbors. Elsa Einstein, forty-five, a broad, plain woman with sparkling blue eyes, was the most gregarious. Her daughters, Ilse and Margot, both in their early twenties, were timid and spent most of their time at home. Albert Einstein always seemed preoccupied. Neighbors were satisfied that the man matched the role—professor of theoretical physics at the Prussian Academy of Sciences.

This was the second marriage for both Albert and Elsa. At least, neighbors *thought* Albert and Elsa were married. There had been gossip that they had not bothered about a wedding. The two girls were by Elsa's first marriage. Albert had two sons by his first wife, but they lived in Switzerland with their mother.

This was rather barren information for the curious women of Haberlandstrasse, but it was all they had until November 7. That morning, the newspapers of Berlin and of all the world announced that a certain Professor A. Einstein had figured out new theories of physics which would radically change Man's ideas about his universe.

The story came from London, from a meeting of eminent scientists. Evidently Einstein had put science in turmoil. Britons had carefully tested one of the major predictions made by his theories, and found it accurate. The consequences were almost outrageous. Newton was in error. Euclid's geometry was obsolete; parallels met; space was curved. And, incredibly, a beam of light could bend.

This was only half the story. Newspapers also revealed that Einstein had been turning out revolutionary ideas for fourteen years. Scientists, however, had kept them in the shadows for their own private discussion. Now the public could share in the secrets. Einstein said that nothing in the whole universe was at rest; that without planets and other matter there would be no space. Everything had to be described as moving relative to something else. Man's notion of time was purely arbitrary, and so was his idea of size and shape. Furthermore, mass was merely bottled energy.

With deceptive simplicity, Einstein had put all his theories under a mild label—"Relativity."

Scientists could be abstract and academic about Relativity. But the people wanted Einstein to account for his boldness, to reassure them, to tell them what it all meant. Scientists were calling him "another Copernicus." The thought of living on earth at the same time with Albert Einstein was exhilarating.

He himself was first warned of the clamor by a gentle tap at the iron door of his attic. It was the tap of a person who had debated intrusion for some time and was fairly certain that the wrong decision had been made.

The scientist showed no sign of hearing, but got up from his chair slowly and sauntered across to the door, carrying a piece of paper covered with mathematical notes. He opened the door with his left hand. His wife said, "I'm sorry, Albertle. The reporters and God knows what other busybodies are downstairs. I can't put them off any longer."

Einstein obediently followed Elsa down from the garret. To be sure he had read in the morning newspaper the story about his theories. But he still could not see why reporters and strangers should be interested in him. Some men are doers and have lively stories to tell. Some men are thinkers; they can only tell what they think about and what conclusions they have reached. Everything Einstein had to say up to that time had been published in the physics journals. Like anyone else, he was a man with arms and legs, but he was totally involved in the search for truth in physics and that was a purely mental activity. Nor did he consider his equipment for the search— his brain—at all outstanding. He was just more stubborn and more passionate about physics than most men.

"They want to know about *you*," Elsa said over her shoulder as they went downstairs. She added with a small chuckle, "They call you a genius. So come on, Herr Genius."

The library was crowded with people carrying pencils and notebooks. A couple of men had cameras. Einstein paused at the doorway and was about to march up the stairs again, when a young chap with blond hair stepped forward.

"If you'll just answer a few questions, Professor. About the English expedition to test your light theory. You must have been very proud of the result?"

Now, how am I supposed to answer that? Oh, yes, I am very proud of myself. I am really a very clever fellow?

"It was gratifying that English scientists should test the theories of a Berlin physicist," said Einstein with a smile.

The reporters then asked about his family, his boyhood, his schooling. Einstein said he didn't feel obliged to discuss his personal life at all. Besides, it was unimportant. After that the interview centered on his work. He explained that there were two theories of Relativity—the special theory concerning space and time which he had developed in 1905, and the general theory revising the laws of gravitation which he had started in 1908 and perfected in 1915.

The English scientists had tested his general theory, especially the prediction that a beam of starlight traveling past the sun on the way to earth would be bent by the sun's gravitational field. The success of the entire theory hinged on how much the beam would be swung off course.

One of the reporters pointed out that on the previous night in London, Sir Joseph John Thomson had called the theory "perhaps the greatest achievement in the history of human thought." Sir Joseph had added, however, that only twelve men in the world understood the theory and he was not one

7

of them.

Einstein conceded that the theory of gravitation was his greatest accomplishment. But he insisted that many of his advanced students at Berlin University understood the theory. And with enough mental application, a layman could understand its main concepts too.

The heart of the matter was Einstein's discovery that gravitation was not a force, as Newton said, but a curved field, a "warp" in space created by a moving body. As a magnet created a magnetic field around it, so did a planet surround itself with a gravitational field. The mass of the moving body determined the structure and extent of the field, and this geometric structure influenced the path of a lesser mass that happened along. Objects took the curved path of least resistance. They were not *forced* anywhere. The sun could be imagined as the hub of a giant velodrome, with the earth cycling around on an outer rim. The thing called space, then, was simply the arrangement of matter and fields. It was essentially geodesic in nature.

Fortunately this theory could be tested against observation. Einstein had realized that he would have to tear up all his equations if his theory was at variance with the test results.

If light had mass, as his special theory insisted, then it should be affected by gravitation. Einstein figured that starlight would be turned through an angle of just under one second and three-quarters of an arc as it passed close to the sun. Newton's law accounted for only half that much. Stars could not be seen during daylight. At night, the sun was absent. A total sun eclipse was needed, therefore, so that the stars near the sun, briefly visible, could be photographed and their apparent positions compared to their normal fixed spots in the night sky. Einstein had suggested such a test as long ago as 1911. Indeed, a group of German astronomers had gone to Russia in 1914 to photograph an eclipse for the star-light comparisons. But World War I started before the day of eclipse and the German scientists were imprisoned.

However, London's Royal Society, which boasted Newton as a past president, was sufficiently intrigued by Einstein's bizarre notion to send teams of scientists across the world for the eclipse studies at the first post-war opportunity. One group went to Sobral, a town in northern Brazil, and the other to Principe, the lonely little Portuguese colony in West Africa's Gulf of Guinea. A total sun eclipse was scheduled for May 29, 1919, in both places.

Arthur Eddington, a brilliant young astronomer and an expert on Relativity, led the expedition to Principe. His notes showed that he had a harrowing time of it. On May 29, Principe was due for a five-minute eclipse starting at two fifteen in the afternoon. By mid-morning, a tropical thunderstorm was drenching the island. Water was pouring down the sides of the canvas tent Eddington had erected over his astrographic telescope and camera. The equipment was set up in an open patio, adjoining the main house of the Roca Sundy cocoa plantation. It wasn't until twenty minutes before eclipse time that Eddington could uncover his apparatus and see the sun through drifting cloud. The moon moved in front of the sun at precisely two fifteen and Eddington made sixteen shots, although he was doubtful whether the star images could be recorded through the cloud screen. Back in London, the Sobral pictures were found to be blurred, but Eddington had one fine print showing a whole scatter of bright stars around the glowing rim of the blacked-out sun. All through the summer and early fall, the British astronomers measured, photographed the fixed stars in the night sky and sweated over the developing tank.

For Einstein, waiting in Berlin, the suspense was building. "Have you by chance heard anything about the British eclipse expedition?" he asked in a letter to his friend Paul Ehrenfest, professor of theoretical physics at Holland's Leyden University. Ehrenfest passed on the query to Hendrik Antoon Lorentz, the revered Dutch master scientist. Lorentz acted as something of an international clearing house for the latest findings in physics.

A short time later Lorentz wired Einstein: "Eddington found star displacement at rim of sun, preliminary measurement between nine-tenths of a second and twice that value."

It was a rather agonizing message because the range covered the shift allowable under Newton's theory as well as Einstein's. But the fact that some light deflection had been measured was good news. Einstein said as much in a postcard sent to his mother in Lucerne, Switzerland, the same day he received the wire.

In late October, having had no further word on the eclipse results, Einstein traveled to Leyden University to lecture and to attend one of Lorentz' celebrated Monday morning talks. He was seated on the stage of the main lecture hall as guest of honor when Lorentz dramatically took the rostrum and gave the final results of the British studies. Einstein was right. Newton's world, governed by laws of push and pull, was now replaced by Einstein's grander and more artistic world of subtle geometry and "friendly persuasion" among the planets.

But the historic meeting at Leyden, cheered by a thousand students and professors, was not covered by the newspapers.

The world had to wait until November 6, when Sir Joseph John Thomson called a joint meeting of his own august Royal Society and the Royal Astronomical Society. All the intelligentsia of London was invited, as well as newspapermen. Alfred North Whitehead, the philosopher, was in the audience and he described the scene when Sir Frank Dyson, the Astronomer Royal, spoke of the eclipse project.

"The whole atmosphere of tense interest was exactly that of the Greek drama," said Whitehead. "We were the chorus commenting on the decree of destiny as disclosed in the development of a supreme incident. There was a dramatic quality in the very staging—the traditional ceremony, and in the background the picture of Newton."

Einstein, the man who triumphed in this drama, suffered graciously the first invasions into his life and time, patiently answering the most irrelevant questions about Relativity. But when the reporters were joined by amateur star-gazers, inventors, politicians, charity workers, long-lost relations, publishers and hollow-cheeked men who wanted to be his disciples, he fled up into his attic. Elsa Einstein was left downstairs to repel the intruders.

"What kind of barbaric nonsense is this?" Einstein demanded of the etching of Newton on his wall.

"My mission is very straightforward, and it could be very profitable for the good professor," a brisk caller told Elsa Einstein at the front door. "I represent a tobacco company and we are interested in bringing out a new line of quality cigars. We want to call them Relativity Cigars. Now we'd like to know whether Professor Einstein would consent to having his picture on the box."

Frau Einstein relayed the request to her husband. From the immediate bulging of his eyes, she gathered he was not pleased with the idea.

In those early days of fame, it seemed to Einstein that the world had adopted Relativity as a new plaything. People could not understand it so they ridiculed it. He was both bewildered and horrified. There was no cute legend attached to the theory; nothing like Newton's apple or Archimedes' bathtub, so one was invented. It seems that poor Hans Schmidt, the local painter, was working on a roof one day when he toppled over and fell, unhurt, into a pile of rubbish. Einstein had seen the accident through his window and immediately rushed outside and asked Hans whether he had felt anything pulling at him while still in mid-air. Hans said no, he had simply fallen. "Ah-ha," Einstein was supposed to have exclaimed, "that proves gravity is not a force."

The bending of light fascinated people no end. At night men stole outdoors secretly and aimed their flashlights at distant trees. Some of them said that they could see the beam of light curving towards the ground. A British magazine ran a cartoon of two sleuths catching a bank-vault thief red-handed by making their torchlight turn a corner, and captioned it: "Elementary, my dear Einstein."

"The Einstein theory has not exactly become a breakfast table topic, nor has Al Jolson begun to chat about it confidentially over the footlights," commented a New York newspaper. "But it is creeping into the cables and the Sunday papers, and nobody is altogether safe who does not have a few of its phrases handy—as defensive weapons at any rate—when run down against a tea table."

Another American paper said that, even though British scientists "seem to have been seized with something like intellectual panic," it was time to use some good old-fashioned Yankee horse sense. After puzzling over the phenomenon of bending light, experts in celestial affairs had come up with the obvious conclusion that the starlight deflection had nothing to do with gravitation. The beam had merely undergone refraction as it passed through the gases around the sun—an illustration of the well-known fact that a coin lying at the bottom of a glass of water is not exactly where it appears to be. These critics did not mention that Eddington had canceled out any refraction ideas with some arithmetic on gas densities. Actually Einstein had many more opponents than proponents in the Relativity uproar. Practicing astronomers said he was a fraud. Sailors, who had long been using the stars for navigation and had always found them in the same place, thought he was insane. Clergymen said the whole theory was irreligious.

In addition, many scientists attacked Relativity on philosophic grounds. Einstein readily admitted that his theories had been born of imagination and intuition. His detractors said this was a highly speculative way to practice physics. They called it quackery. The only laws of nature worth their salt were those deduced from observation, experience and experiment.

"By their fruits ye shall know them," replied Einstein, meaning both physicists and their theories. Relativity had predicted accurately a complex trick of nature perpetrated ninety-three million miles away. It involved a measurement comparable to the thickness of a match seen from half a mile. Surely, that proved the value of Relativity, and of Einstein's intuition as well.

During all this controversy, thousands of thoughtful men, scientists and laymen alike, examined Relativity for themselves. They made sketches in newspaper margins to help them visualize Einstein's universe. For many, it was a first adventure into physics and a surprisingly exciting one.

The broad ideas involved in the general theory, the gravitation theory, were not difficult to understand. It was the special theory that sent brains cart wheeling. This theory had glamor and mystique because it revealed man's counting of time as significant only to his own planet. Einstein represented eternity as already laid out. Man was journeying through what Einstein called "the space-time continuum" of eternity and the universe. An unsigned article in the British magazine *Nature* gave this concept the best interpretation:

"At this moment rain is falling, leaves are rustling, a motor hurries along the road, the clouds are drifting. All is change in motion. It seems that all history is change, and all is hurrying by as we stand. But is it not a truer view, certainly a less egoistic one, to see history as one eternal whole, and ourselves as voyagers through it, our vision of it ever changing. . . . ? All our pictures and conceptions of the universe in time and space are but pictures, and the painters are many . . . We go to a picture gallery; there is so much of difference that at first there seems little in common. Yet gradually we become conscious that the pictures are all drawn from a common life. We begin to be able to analyze the painters, and see what kind of mind is looking out upon the life, to detect a point of view. In so doing we grow more clear as to the one reality behind all the pictures . . . This is a true parable of the great change that has been consummated in physical thought by Einstein's work . . . It is the recognition of the relativity of our space-and-time pictures that has clarified our understanding of the universal phenomena. In Einstein's world the commonest phenomena become organic parts of a great plan. The rationality of the universe becomes an exciting romance, not a cold dogma."

To share in this romance, men tussled with the special theory of relativity until they conquered it. Their reasoning was raw and their final exposition somewhat home-made. But even in the rough, it was, as Einstein said, a beautiful theory.

Newton said space and time were absolute. Space was motionless. Time moved evenly, everywhere and at all times. And, before Einstein, matter and energy seemed well examined. Matter was made of atoms, billions of them. An atom was indestructible and inconvertible. Energy in its various manifestations was described in words and equations.

James Clerk Maxwell, Scottish physicist, made it clear that

light consisted of electromagnetic waves. Man had decided that the waves were carried by motionless, all-pervading ether. A couple of Americans, Michelson and Morley, wanted to test the resistance this ether offered to the progress of earth through space. Logically, earth should be bucking a twenty-mile-a-second head ether wind because this was earth's orbiting speed relative to the sun. Light was propagated through the ether, therefore the velocity of a beam of light should be slowed by the ether slip stream if it were fired in the direction of the earth's motion. If it were shot in the other direction, the ether tail wind should increase its speed.

The Americans raced light rays forward in the direction of the earth's motion and sideways at right angles to it, bouncing them off mirrors and racing them back again. It was a dead heat. Yet any summer oarsman knows he will take longer to row upstream and down than cross-stream and back. It should have been the same with the light rays and the ether stream. But exact measurements showed that head wind or tail wind did not affect the speed of light. It clocked 186,000 miles a second all the time.

There were two easy explanations: either there was no ether or the earth stood still. Scientists could not accept either, so they dreamed up various ways to reconcile ether and the failure of light to detect it. At the time of the American experiment Einstein was still a backward child. The puzzle was not cleared up until he was twenty-five years old.

Then, for a start, he decided that if ether could not be detected—and that was virtually proven—it should not be included in Man's calculations. So forget ether. The American experiment had simply proved that the speed of light was constant. It was not affected in any way by the dash of earth through space. Newton's laws of mechanics worked perfectly and gave accurate predictions about all sorts of celestial mischief without taking into account the motion of the planet or any other uniformly moving body to which they were applied. The same thing was true of light. Its velocity remained at 186,000 miles a second whatever the speed of the source. There was no question of adding velocities where light was concerned. A light flashed from a star to earth would still travel here at 186,000 miles a second even if the star happened at the same time to be racing towards earth at 100,000 miles a second. Two plus two do not always equal four. So now Einstein made the flat pronouncement that all natural laws—optical and mechanical—are the same for all systems that are in motion relative to each other.

It follows that if light will not change its speed, then it cannot be used in a comparative way to measure the velocity of anything else. Man has to face the fact that, of all systems in the universe including the lordly sun and the friendly earth and the vast moving gravitational frames, there is not one of them that can be taken as an absolute point of reference to measure the absolute speeds and directions of the other systems. The movement of Mars can be described in relation to the movement of other planets, but man cannot be more definite than that. And because all motion is relative, with no favored systems, there can be no such thing as absolute rest. That relegates so-called stationary space to nothingness.

This is in fact the guts of Relativity.

But even though the speed of light is constant, it is not instantaneous. When Michelson and Morley, using the same source, shot their light beams forward and sideways to mirrors, the forward moving light ray had to go further. While it was traveling, the mirror was moving away from the point of source with the orbiting speed of earth. Of course, the light could easily overtake the sluggish mirror but some extra distance was involved. The vertical light ray could follow a shorter diagonal route to reach its mirror. Yet the rays still came a dead heat. If their actual speed did not vary, then the only possible explanation seemed to lie in the measuring rods used as the "tracks" in the experiment. Specifically, the measuring rod facing the direction of motion of the earth, the horizontal track, must be a tiny fraction shorter than the vertical track to make up for the difference in traveling times. It must *shrink* in the direction of motion. By extension, this strange occurrence must apply to any moving object or any object attached to a moving system. The greater the velocity, the more contraction takes place.

An earth man cannot notice this shrinkage because he is a part of the same moving system, traveling with the same velocity and suffering the same shrinkage. But let's suppose some sort of man lives on another planet. He would be attuned to a different system, accustomed to his own standards of measurement. If he has telescopic eyes, and it may be that he has, he could look across to see earth speeding by and wonder why a salesman is selling a yard rule that by his estimate might be only thirty-five inches long. A bowling ball would seem to him an ellipse, a fat man not so fat. Such speculation is not so strange really if a rod or a ball is thought of—not as solid—but merely as a great conglomeration of atoms jostled about by motion. Again, this emphasizes that Man's impression of the physical nature of the universe and its furniture is no more than an impression.

Regard once more that horizontal light beam traveling the first lap between source and mirror. Man has given that distance a greater length than it might appear to an inhabitant of another planet. He has also given the duration of the trip a greater time value, because the distance traveled by the light beam divided by the time of the trip must equal the constant speed of light. Thus, Man has not only a subjective idea of distance but also a subjective idea of time. The faster his movement, the slower his clock runs. Obviously, if the observer on the neighbor planet perceived a shorter distance, he would estimate a shorter time for the light connection. To this fellow, the earth man's clock would seem to be running slow.

Time and distance, therefore, are both relative qualities, totally dependent on the motion of the particular system to which they belong.

Einstein's equations also revealed that along with shrinkage and time slow-down, moving bodies picked up mass (weight) proportionate to their speed. This was a protective measure invented by nature so that nothing could reach the speed of light. The faster something moves, the heavier it becomes. It would take an impossible, infinite force to accelerate a body past the light barrier.

Faster motion produces more mass. Motion is energy, therefore the extra mass is really extra energy. Then all mass is congealed energy. A cup, a pencil, a mountain chalet—it doesn't matter what kind of mass—the dormant energy is there. How much energy? Determine the mass, then multiply by the square of the velocity of light. The musical equation said: $E = MC^2$.

These were some of the startling Einstein theories revealed to the world in 1919. This was why he was suddenly famous. He was the world's new genius, the maestro of the abstract, the wizard of mathematics. He wandered in places where nobody could follow. But then he was not a man like other men, this Einstein. He was a freak, a wonderful freak . . .

The man was drowned in the myth, although, as Einstein himself said, "A man should look for what is, and not for what he thinks should be . . ."

CHAPTER 2

ESCAPE TO THE UNIVERSE

"I was born in Ulm," Einstein said, "an old city on the Danube, with narrow winding streets and the smell of the leather works and the good air of old times."

His birthday was March 14, 1879, and Pauline and Hermann Einstein were glad to have him. He was their first child.

The father looked like a severe bandmaster. He wore pince-nez with black tape, and a thick black mustache that swept the full arc of his top lip. He had a stiff-necked way of carrying himself. It was all show. Albert remembered him as "extremely friendly, mild, wise, patient, charming and good." Hermann managed a small electrochemical works, but at the time of Albert's birth he was preparing to go into business for himself.

Pauline Einstein was an able *hausfrau* and a splendid pianist. Later on, her playing of Mozart was one of the few distractions that could make Albert take his head out of a book. She was not a comely woman—her nose was too broad, but it was from his mother that Albert inherited his soft, brown, tranquil eyes and his luxuriant hair. Pauline was a Koch. Like the Einsteins, the Koches could not boast any distinguished sons. Both families had been living around Swabia for as long as anyone could remember. They farmed or sold cloth or clerked in banks. At night, the men liked to drink beer and talk and perhaps read Schiller aloud. Schiller was the most famous product of the region. The women seemed to be always involved in household chores. Weekends, they would walk in the woods, punt on the Danube, attend an open-air concert, and worry that Ulm was getting far too industrialized. They were gentle, unhurried people who reflected the serenity of southwest Germany before the distant northerners spoiled things.

Once asked to draw up a family tree, Albert Einstein replied: "I couldn't even if I wanted to. I really know nothing about my forebears."

The most unusual thing about the Einsteins was that they were Jewish. They did not go to the synagogue and they did not observe the dietary laws. But their Jewishness set them apart from the majority in Swabia and the gulf widened soon after Albert was born, when Pauline and Hermann Einstein moved to Munich, a predominantly Catholic city.

Hermann had a rare run of business luck in Munich and within five years he and his brother Jacob, who lived with the family, owned a fairly prosperous electrical engineering plant. Now they could afford to employ men. Life was good all around. The Einsteins lived in a tall stone house, surrounded by a large and unkempt garden, on the outskirts of the city. A daughter, Maja, had arrived, and Albert, who had been backward in learning to walk and talk, was even then beginning to emerge as a personality.

Right from the start he was intrigued by nature. He had an insatiable interest in trees and running brooks and anything that was invented and controlled by God, whom he supposed to be sitting somewhere above the clouds in a great granite armchair.

The numerous cousins who came to visit in the big house from Swabia and from another Einstein settlement in northern Italy and the few little boys in the neighborhood who tried to befriend Albert found him dull. Marbles did not excite him and if anyone suggested a game of soldiers, he would just turn on his heel and paddle away. He tended to paddle because he had large feet. He could sit on his haunches by the hour and watch the labors of an ant colony. Entire days would be spent in trying to win the confidence of the flock of dusty white chickens that bustled hungrily about the backyard. Albert was a "loner" by preference. However, he adored his sister Maja who looked enough like him to be a twin.

The boy was about six when one of those landmarks of life, so prized by psychiatrists, occurred. He had been in bed for days with a bronchial infection when his father gave him a little mariner's compass. Hermann said that Albert could pretend to be a ship's captain lashed to the wheel in a storm, bringing home his good old ship, and he could pretend to dash the water out of his eyes every now and again and see the trusty compass. Albert was uninspired. But he wondered why the nervous needle always pointed to the big N. His Uncle Jacob told him about magnetic fields and the two poles of earth, but one question inevitably led to another and after a while Jacob

23

had to quit. "Well, that's just the way things are," was his final plea for silence.

Albert remained unsatisfied and carried the compass around for weeks. "Young as I was," he said later, "the memory of that compass never left me."

Despite his questing mind, young Albert was a flop as a schoolboy. He was clever at literature and arithmetic because they interested him. But he would sit through his language and history lessons without absorbing a thing. Nor did he pretend to be learning. His inattentiveness incensed the teachers who had a holy regard for discipline. They called him "Herr Lang-weil" meaning "Mister Dullard," and he referred to them, secretly, as "sergeants."

"It would be nice if you could leave us, Einstein," a teacher suggested one day.

"But I have done nothing wrong," the boy said.

The teacher twitched his mouth. "Nothing bad enough to get you expelled," he admitted. "It could happen though. Your presence and your dreamy ho-hum attitude toward everything we are trying to do and teach here is undermining the respect of the whole class."

It was a Catholic primary school and Albert was the only Jew in his class. He received instruction in the Christian faith along with the rest of the boys. On one occasion, near Easter, a teacher held up three large, rusty nails. "These are the nails the Jews used to crucify Jesus," he thundered. Albert was shocked. It was his first experience with anti-Semitism. He was impressed with Jesus as a man and wondered what He would have said if He had been in the classroom when the nails were produced.

Albert shunned sports and gymnastics. It was always simply a matter of one boy against another, to see who could do the most push ups or jump the highest. He had an innate dislike for anything competitive. But in sports the other boys sided with the teachers. They nicknamed Albert *biedermeier*—meaning, in modern slang, "a square."

He did not care what he was called. He knew he was being ridiculed. But before he got around to deciding whether to do anything about it, he would become preoccupied with something like the shadow cast by a flagpole. Einstein later remembered that a boy once tried to shake his aloofness.

"I could make you do whatever I wanted with just one look," this boy, a large fellow with small eyes, challenged.

"I'm sorry but you've got me all wrong," Einstein said mildly, smiling. "How you look doesn't interest me one bit."

The husky boy walked away muttering that it was impossible to understand such a weird person.

The things Einstein hated most about school were the rigidity of the school curriculum and the garrison atmosphere. "It is bad," he said later, "for a school to work with methods of fear, force and artificial authority. They destroy the sincerity and self-confidence of the pupil. They produce submissive persons."

He liked to puzzle things out for himself. For instance, Jacob, noting his interest in arithmetic, had given him a book of algebra. The boy was fascinated and solved every problem in the book. Then his uncle introduced him to geometry via the Pythagoras Theory. Reciting the theory over and over,

Albert went off and proved it by his own wit.

At this time music was an integral part of daily life in the Einstein household and Albert found it a wonderful relaxation. He took violin lessons from the age of seven. Very slowly he mastered the instrument; his playing became sweet and sure. Like his mother, Albert found music "an inner necessity."

During Einstein's eleventh year, Max Talmey came into his life. Max was the brother of the family physician; he had recently arrived in Munich to study medicine at the University. He was a shy, bookish man of twenty-one, a Jew with few friends. Eagerly he accepted Hermann Einstein's invitation to twice-weekly dinners and in a short time he had taken over Jacob's role as Albert's answer man. Jacob did not mind because the electrical business had started downhill and he and Hermann were fully engrossed in trying to keep afloat.

In the five years that Max took to complete his medical course, he helped mold a genius. Nobody ever had a more willing student.

"In all those years," Max later wrote, "I never saw Albert reading any light literature. Nor did I ever see him in the company of schoolmates or other boys his own age."

Einstein's own summation of that momentous period was, "I had a furious impulse to understand, to be informed."

Immediately Max recognized the boy's interest in the workings of the world. He bought him a series of books on natural science. Albert's brain was still swimming through these, when Max found him a book called *Force and Matter*, explaining the history and accomplishments of physics. He followed it with a text on advanced geometry. Night after night, season after season, Albert sat before his bedroom lamp reading and re-reading the books. Maja and the chickens in the backyard lost their friend. His father shrugged in dismay. His mother worried about his pallor.

After a time, Albert transferred to the Luitpold Gymnasium, a high school which professed to teach along humanist lines. The curriculum didn't satisfy him. The school subjects seemed sterile compared to what he was learning at home. He refused now to memorize lessons just for the sake of passing examinations. Mathematics had taught him to reason and he wanted to examine thoroughly every "fact" in the text books to make sure it was not just supposition.

Inevitably, he started to question religion. "How do we *know* there is a God?" he asked. There was a rabbi attached to the gymnasium and young Einstein had long talks with him, but his question was never fully answered. His father did not help, either. Papa Einstein was casual about religion. This bothered Albert. Faith was such a vital thing. He was a lonely boy and he needed God for comfort and for friendship. He was very reluctant to stop believing in Him. Yet the more he delved into Max's books, the more he worried about the validity of the Bible. He made excuses for the apparent errors. But it did no good.

One night he sat up late, a boy of twelve alone with his thoughts. *There is no God.* The Bible spoke of an anthropomorphic or man-like God. Adam and Eve had heard Him *walking* in the Garden of Eden. Albert could not accept this. His natural science books, following logic and proof, gave a version of Genesis and the making of Man in which God,

Adam and Eve had no part. The Bible could not be trusted as a factual book. It said that Moses got water out of a rock, that Jonah lived inside a whale. Albert knew these things were scientifically impossible.

He snuffed out the light and sat in the darkness for a long time. His mind raced fitfully, getting nowhere. He could hear the wind in the trees outside. The moon was high in the east. The world still functioned, not only smoothly but artistically. Without God, the world might be expected to career like a runaway horse. But it didn't. Einstein went to bed that night without saying his prayers.

"After this," he said later, "I started on a positively fanatic orgy of free thinking, coupled with the idea that youth is intentionally being deceived by the state through lies. It was a crushing experience. I suspected every kind of authority. I was skeptical about even general convictions. But one thing was clear. The religious paradise of my early youth, now lost, was a first attempt to rise above a self-centered existence."

Young Einstein was a boy in transition. He yearned for something to believe in, something reliable. He could find it only in nature. "Out yonder there was this huge world, which exists independently of us human beings and which stands before us like a great, eternal riddle. I decided to devote myself to the inspection of this world." His resolve gave him new security and increased his independence of other people. He was content to see the mystery of the universe as God and he expressed his religion as "humility and admiration for the superior intellect that reveals itself in world harmony."

"The most beautiful experience we can have is the mysterious," he said. "It is the fundamental emotion which stands at the cradle of true art and true science. Whoever does not know it and can no longer wonder, no longer marvel, is as good as dead, and his eyes are dimmed. A knowledge of the existence of something we cannot penetrate, our primitive perceptions of the profoundest Reason and the most radiant beauty —it is this knowledge and this emotion that constitute true religious feeling."

These thoughts were building in Einstein's mind as he pored over his books in his Munich bedroom. Max Talmey was outdistanced now but he could still sense the boy's needs. If he wanted to seek fresh knowledge, he had better learn more about the mind. Max introduced Albert to philosophy with a copy of Immanuel Kant's *Critique of Pure Reason.*

Einstein learned of the pitfalls that accompanied man's power to reason, the subjectivity of apparently objective observations. He saw the dangers of prejudice.

Kant had decided that man-found laws of science which stood up to test derived from the inventive element of human reason as well as from experience. Einstein chewed on this thought for a long time. If the human mind could invent as well as reason logically, then intuition and imagination were the keys to creation. They could play tricks, but they could also lead to the discovery of a truth that had not been known before. Einstein agreed with Hume, another philosopher he read, that man might never know the true causes behind the effects. But intuition could give a deep-hidden insight into causes and if it could point to effects, then that was enough.

The heavy reading Einstein did in his teen years might have

crumbled the brain of anyone else. He was driven to learn as much as he could, as quickly as he could—and he didn't quite understand why. He studied the prophets—Moses, Confucius, Buddha, Christ, and the philosophers—Socrates, Aristotle, Spinoza, Voltaire, Schopenhauer. Most of his excitement, however, came from his books on mathematics, physics and geometry.

Hermann Einstein tried to coax his son into practical study. He planned for him a career in electrical engineering. Albert barely listened. His mind never left his books.

In the summer after his fifteenth birthday, he was called down to the living room for a family council. His father's business had failed. Hermann would have to sell the house to pay his debts and then move to Milan, where his cousins could help him make a fresh start.

Albert was secretly pleased. He hated his garrison school, but even worse was the knowledge that in less than three years he faced conscription into the German army. Even one day as a German soldier would be too much. Six months or a year would be agony. An escape to Italy would remove all such worry.

"Unfortunately," his father continued, "only your mother and I and Maja can go at this time. You'll have to stay behind in Munich, at least for a year—until you are ready for a university."

That was that. Albert's only real friends, his immediate family, went south to the sunshine. By then, Max Talmey had graduated and left Munich to seek an internship in a country hospital. Albert boarded out in a small room in the house of a woman he hardly knew. He sought solace in his books, but it was not enough. His detachment from other people was not as complete as he had thought. He was lonely and miserable now. And as he watched soldiers boot clicking through the city, his depression became unbearable. He dreamed up an idea which would get him out of his Munich prison and down to Italy.

He persuaded Max's brother to give him a doctor's order saying that he needed a drier climate for a lung condition, one recommending Italy. Armed with this spurious document, Albert approached the school principal and brazenly asked for a certificate in mathematics. He admitted he was below standard in history, geography and languages, but private study in mathematics had put him into integral calculus while the rest of his class was still doing repeating decimals.

The principal regarded Albert as a difficult student, to say the least, but he was well aware of his mathematical prowess. It irritated the teachers. So, mostly because the Luitpold Gymnasium was anxious to get rid of him, Albert walked out with an official letter saying he was qualified in mathematics to enter a university. Within the hour, he was on a train to Milan.

The year he spent in Italy was one of the best of his life. He walked, read, lazed in the sun and avoided his father every time he got that how-about-earning-a-living look behind his pince-nez. The boy kept putting the future out of his mind, roaming the Apennines and squatting in the dust to talk to peasants who lived in caves and ate black bread. Their world was wind and rain and buds on the olive trees, and so, in a different way, was his.

The bond of affection and understanding between Albert and Maja became strong and lasting. He would tell her what he had read about nature and she would listen with steady, round eyes. At night, watching the stars, Albert would tell her how long it took for the light from a star to reach earth.

"Now what do you suppose it would be like if you could sit on the front end of a light beam and travel with it through the night?" he asked.

"Well," said Maja, eager to play the game, "it would be like waving a magic wand and seeing the world light up before you."

Albert laughed and said that if he ever figured out a way to do that, she should share the ride with him.

In the late summer of 1895, Hermann Einstein, still broke, persuaded a cousin to put up twenty dollars a month for Albert to continue his education. The boy refused to return to Germany, so it was decided he should take a general engineering course at the Polytechnic Academy in Zurich. His letter from Munich permitted him to qualify for the entrance examination.

In a fresh check suit, Albert went off by train, a bag of books and a case of clothes banging at each knee. The magnificent Swiss countryside drew him to the window all the way to Zurich. The city itself reminded him of a page from a Gutenberg Bible—substantial, but with a sort of restrained flourish. He found a cheap pension and registered for his entrance test with his fingers crossed.

He flunked. However, the examiner was so impressed with the boy's mathematics that he had him enrolled at a small liberal arts school in Aarau. If Albert worked well, he could return to the Polytechnic in a year with the proper matriculation certificate.

The school at Aarau was as different from the one in Munich as a writers' colony is different from a newspaper rewrite desk. The success of the school depended entirely on a man's personal drive to accomplish something. It was a very successful school.

Einstein rented a room in the home of one of the teachers, a man called Winteler, and the teacher's son Paul, also sixteen, became his first close male friend of his own age. He liked him so much that he introduced him to Maja during her later visit to Switzerland. Eventually she became Mrs. Winteler.

In the pleasant atmosphere of Aarau, Einstein started to plan his life from a practical point of view. "Frankly," he wrote his parents, "the idea of becoming a professional man in any of the engineering fields depresses me. But I think I could qualify as a science teacher. To this end, I hope to take scientific subjects at the Polytechnic and then become a Swiss citizen."

On his second attempt he had no trouble getting into the famous college, and then began four years devoted to physics. This made him a young hermit in the liveliest student town in Europe. When he was not in the lecture room or the physics laboratory, he shut himself up in his small room at a boarding house and doggedly studied every single thing that Man had found out about the workings of the universe. Only occasionally would he join a few friends and go to the Cafe Metropole. This was a coffee house and student haunt on the river front full of talk about politics, professors and poetry.

The school insisted on certain standards of dress and Albert complied with a suit, tie and high-wing collar. His pants were always crumpled and his waistcoat lacked a button or two, but he was still sartorially average. He was also average in height and the way he wore his black curly hair, thick and uncombed, was common style, too. He was even average as a student, mainly because he cut so many classes and because he rarely took notes.

By this time he had decided to become a physics teacher and a theoretical physicist in his spare time. He felt he already had enough basic mathematics for this, so he cut his mathematics lectures. Hermann Minkowski, the Russian geometry wizard, was one of the lecturers during Einstein's four years in Zurich. He upbraided the youth for neglecting his studies and warned him he would regret it later.

It was a fortunate accident that Einstein's closest friends at the institute were both majoring in mathematics. One was Marcel Grossman who was genuinely awed by the range of Einstein's mind. Grossman had a gift for getting to the crux of any new problem and working out conclusions for himself, but he conceded that Einstein had an even greater talent for this. Grossman, however, got better marks because he stuck to the set curriculum. He tried to convince his friend that this was the only way to pass examinations, but Einstein stubbornly went his own way. Generously, Grossman took detailed notes on all lectures and drummed them into Einstein at the weekends. He was a captive audience then. Grossman's family lived in Zurich and Marcel would take Albert home to give him a good meal. Einstein ate only once or twice a day during the week. He just could not be bothered with food.

His other close friend was Mileva Maric, a petite, dark-haired, dark-eyed girl from the North Serbian town of Novi Sad. She was as good at mathematics as Marcel and she, too, helped in the weekend coaching sessions. Einstein admired her independence. Although she came from a wealthy family —her father was a judge, she had made her way alone to Zurich and joined the college as one of the very few female students. She hoped to qualify as a mathematics teacher and to live in Switzerland.

Friends said Mileva and Albert were attracted to each other because of their opposite natures. Albert's preoccupation with physics made him hopelessly impractical. He could never make up his mind about everyday matters and would usually agree with the last person to whom he had spoken simply out of plain disinterest. One time Mileva suggested a picnic in the country with a group of students. Albert said that would be fine. Later Marcel said it would be too cold for a picnic and a concert would be better. Albert agreed. Then Mileva came back and said the weather would be perfect for a picnic. "I'm looking forward to it," said Albert.

Albert was equally erratic about people. A student would get into a discussion with him, feel a rapport and regard Albert as a new friend. The next time he came along, Albert would hardly remember him; at least that was the impression he gave.

Mileva, on the other hand, was decisive about everything. She judged people quickly and was firm in her likes and dislikes. She had a definite viewpoint in any argument. She planned her studies and her routine well ahead. She tried to bring a sense of order into Albert's life, too. The mathematics instruction was only part of it. She made him eat regularly and told him how to budget his allowance properly. Frequently, she was infuriated at his absent-mindedness. He would look at this angry little girl stamping her foot and a glint of devilment would come into his eyes. He would make a joke or pull a face and slowly charm her out of her mood.

By their final year at the Polytechnic, they were deeply in love. Part of Albert's heart was forever lost to physics, but the other part belonged to Mileva. She gave herself totally. Her personal ambition had faded. Both wanted marriage and children as soon as possible after Albert's graduation. Mileva was pleased with Albert's chosen career as a theoretical physicist. She was fully aware of his brilliant mind. So, too, were their friends—Grossman and Maurice Solovine, a Frenchman taking the physics course, and Friedrich Adler, an Austrian who mixed his physics with talks on socialism at the Cafe Metropole.

Einstein hoped he would be hired after graduation as an assistant to one of the physics professors. He had already broached the subject and received some encouragement, although he was jokingly told that he seemed so skeptical about everything in the text books that there would soon be nothing left to teach.

His mind was like a fine sieve. He did not accept anything unless it passed his rigid mental cross-examination. Mostly, he was troubled by physicists who insisted on extending theories and announcing new "truths" without proving first the validity of the basic theories. He was also wary of scientists who used a "common-sense" approach to physics. Always in the back of his mind was Schopenhauer's testy saying that Man's idea of the world was just that—an idea. "What he knows is not a sun and an earth, but only an eye that sees a sun, a hand that feels an earth," said Schopenhauer.

Man's gift of vision, for instance, was splendid but not in any way absolute. The German professor Wilhelm Röntgen, had just discovered the X ray which could pass right through a man's body and project the shadows of his bones on a photographic plate. How different would be Man's idea of the world around him if he had X-ray vision.

Einstein responded to an essay published by Ernst Mach, professor of philosophy at the University of Vienna. Mach said science should clean house. Toss out all the theories that Man could not verify by experiment. Knock the scientific pyramid down to the proven base and build again before outsiders scoffed and hailed the rebirth of alchemy. Einstein joined Mach at the prosecution bench and, in informal physics discussions at the Polytechnic, the professors soon learned that they must defend any theory when Einstein was around.

"Ah, yes, of course, Einstein. It may seem ambitious to formulate the properties of the ether when we haven't proven its actual existence, but we need the ether to explain light waves. We do, however, appreciate the spirit with which you tackle these . . ."

Damn that boy for his infernal skepticism!

CHAPTER 3

RELATIVITY IS BORN

Albert Einstein graduated from the Zurich Polytechnic in the spring of 1900 and faced the workaday world as a twenty-one-year-old misfit. His family circle in Italy sent congratulations and stopped the monthly allowance. He was on his own now.

Two other students had been selected above Einstein as assistants on the physics staff. Grossman and Adler had lobbied for their friend unsuccessfully. In any case, the hard cramming Einstein had to do in his final semester to pass the mathematics examinations had made him weary of schools. In fact, he had cooled on his decision to become a teacher.

He had no taste for any conventional job. Instead, he wanted to spend his life investigating nature. But even in this familiar field, he was filled with doubts. He feared he might not be capable of discovery. The best thing was to earn a living and follow his first desire in his spare time. He felt he might be happy as either a shoemaker or a lighthouse keeper. Both jobs offered "thinking time." Mileva told him both ideas were impractical. He should find something for which he was qualified. Mileva was still getting an allowance from home. She agreed to delay marriage until Albert found a regular job.

Work was not easy to find then and Einstein had to take what he could get. He was hired temporarily to make calculations for the director of the Zurich Observatory; then, for another six months he relieved a professor at a technical school in the nearby city of Winterthur. The boys in the mathematics class decided to make sport of the new young teacher. On the first day they talked and jostled and took no notice of him. Einstein called the rowdiest youth to the blackboard, winked at the class and asked the boy to solve a simple problem. The boy was a natural show-off and jotted down the answer with a flourish. For ten minutes then, Einstein fired one question after another. The boy started well and, with all eyes on him, tried to show how clever he was. Soon, however, his answers came slower and slower, his thoughts grew muddled, his writing frantic and then he was puffing hard. Finally he gave up with tears in his eyes.

"He has a lot to learn, doesn't he?" Einstein observed as the boy walked back to his desk. After that, the class was quiet.

At Winterthur, Einstein also made a modest start as a seeker of truth. He wrote a learned essay on capillarity and had it published on Page 513 of Volume IV of the ultra-academic German physics monthly, *Annalen der Physik.* (Water sits flat and calm in a drinking glass except at the edges where it clings a fraction up the sides of the glass— that is capillarity. Einstein was intrigued with such tricks of nature and solving them was one of his favorite ways of relaxing.)

On the day in 1901 when the article was published, Einstein went to Zurich to take out his papers making him a Swiss citizen. He had been a resident for the required five years. He was also eligible now for his compulsory three months' service in the Swiss Army—a duty native-born Swiss fulfilled at eighteen. This time Einstein was actually eager to be drafted. There was nothing brutal or Spartan about this army; it certainly was not aggressive. Military duty was more like a game —three months to start and then two or three weeks each year playing soldier in the mountains. And the men were allowed to keep their equipment at home.

Einstein presented himself proudly at the induction center and stripped off his shirt for the doctor. Months of sparse eating—more from neglect than from necessity—had left him scrawny. He was rejected. Einstein argued that he was perfectly well. The doctor said there were more than enough robust men to fill the quota without taking the thin ones as well.

Mileva tried to comfort him. She reminded him that his hatred for the military was the prime reason he had run away from Munich. Why was he so anxious to join the Swiss Army? Albert said the doctor had no right to turn him down. Mileva gave up. Sometimes he acted like a child.

Einstein went north now to the resort town of Schaffhausen to teach general subjects in a boarding school for rich children. The pay was miserly. A friend of Einstein's, who had been through the same mill, said the young physicist "earned too little to live and too much to die."

Early in 1902, Albert was fired because his method of teaching was "too informal." A few weeks later his father died and Albert spent his last few francs on train fare to Italy. He lingered with his family there a while, studying the worn physics books that now seemed as much part of him as the black mustache above his top lip. He scribbled notes and equations on scraps of paper, sharpening his wits on various thermodynamic problems. *Annalen der Physik* accepted two of his essays and Einstein began to hope that perhaps by hard work and stubborn application he could bring really fresh material to the science of physics. But he still worried about how to earn a livelihood.

He appealed to Marcel Grossman for help, writing that he had all sorts of promising ideas running riot in his brain. "Perhaps they won't amount to anything," he added. "But I feel that I must work them out to their limits. All I need for the work is a favorable environment and a little luck, although I have no idea how the first might be obtained."

Grossman took his friend's letter to his father who wrote to an old colleague, Friedrich Haller, director of the Swiss Patent Office in Berne, recommending Einstein for the job of examiner.

In the late summer of 1902, Einstein walked into Haller's office for his interview with his heart thumping.

"Tell me, Herr Einstein, have you had any experience in technical work?"

"None."

It was a poor start. Some of the inventions and devices to

be examined would be highly complex mechanical gadgets. But Haller, a bluff, good-natured fellow, took a liking to Einstein in their two hour talk and gave him the job.

Within six months, Albert and Mileva were married. Friends had noticed a change in Mileva's attitude and thought the romance might be doomed. Something had happened between the two, but Mileva would only say that it was "intensely personal." Whatever it was, she brooded about it and Albert seemed to be in some way responsible. Friends encouraged Mileva to talk about her problem and to get it out in the open. She insisted that it was too personal and kept it a secret all her life—a vital detail in the story of Albert Einstein that still remains shrouded in mystery.

Mileva married Albert despite the incident. She knew her love for the man was strong enough to survive. She did not think of the shadow her "experience" would cast over their life together.

There was no money and no time for a honeymoon, so the couple immediately set up household in a small flat by the Aar River.

Like a thousand other Swiss civil servants, Albert went off each day in a cheap suit, with a lunch of bread and butter tucked under his arm in a paper bag. He sat at his desk through the daylight hours, studying new patent submissions, comparing them with devices already in the catalogues, making his merit report. He discovered that he liked gadgetry. He became very interested in his job. Haller found his reports expert and exact and clear. Einstein was soon given the tougher assignments and an increase in pay. He examined several worthwhile inventions. One, he recalled later, was an improved slide rule.

A gentle, lovable Italian engineer, Michele Besso, was Einstein's desk neighbor at the office. The two men talked physics during the slack periods. Sometimes after work, they went to a cafe patronized by university professors and assistants for talk and coffee. It was always coffee because Einstein did not drink wine and he regarded beer as poison. Tobacco, on the other hand, was part of his diet. He was addicted to cigars— the longest, fattest, blackest ones he could find. He smoked one after the other so that, even as a young man, his teeth were stained brown and his throat was raw. His voice became weaker, but still he did not stop smoking.

Mileva and Albert occasionally had Besso and other friends home for a musical evening. Albert still practiced the violin; his playing was clean and good. Mileva did not play an instrument, but she enjoyed music and she liked conversation. She would start the guests off on a subject she knew interested Albert and then sit and listen. He argued with gusto and laughed uproariously at the least excuse. A friend later recalled: "He was always close to a strong expression of life one way or another."

"Have I told you the joke about the old whore . . ." he would start off in front of his men and women guests.

"Albert!" Mileva would object.

And then he would hoot with laughter because he had only set out to shock Mileva. Friends saw them as an ideal couple— the steady Mileva and the unpredictable Albert. Like other newly weds, they spoke love in across-the-room glances. They had their own foolish, warm little secrets. Pickled herring, for instance. Albert loved it. If Mileva had prepared it for the late supper with guests, Albert would take the biggest chunk and steal a look at his wife.

In 1904, they had a son, Hans Albert. The father was delighted and he walked the infant all over town in the baby carriage.

But then it was Einstein's turn to produce. Relativity was stirring in his brain. He had worked constantly on his physics, far into a thousand nights, since he left school. He knew everything that had been discovered or simply suggested. His method was to work from basic truths and try every conceivable deduction, no matter how ridiculous it seemed. His genius lay in picking the root concepts that pointed the way to greater truths. His imagination conjured up the various approaches. His intuition told him when he was on the right track. It was that way with Relativity—a step at a time. Everything suggested that there was no such condition in the world as absolute rest. What does that lead to? He worked on and on through 1904. One puzzle led to another. His brain was on fire. His body was exhausted. He could not eat. He could not sleep. *The speed of light never varies.* When people spoke to him, he did not hear. He wandered about in a daze. At times, he wondered if this was the way to insanity.

He tried to rest by concentrating on other problems. One resulting thesis, "New Determination of Molecular Dimensions," won him his doctor of philosophy degree from Zurich.

Another paper cleared up mysteries about light and advanced Berlin Professor Max Planck's new and revolutionary quantum theory.

Planck said radiation did not come in waves, as was generally supposed, but in packets of corpuscles (quanta), each containing a definite amount of energy. Einstein saw this theory as a stepping stone. It had been proven. It could be extended. He said a beam of light was in reality a train of quanta, a shower of particles. Scientists, who had long insisted that light traveled only in waves, scoffed when Einstein's latest work appeared. But the theory stuck—and so did the word Einstein coined for light's tiny packets of energy, "photons."

This one paper was sufficient to make Einstein a great physicist. He had made his first big strike. Yet he could not relax and enjoy his success because of Relativity.

Frustration drove him out to wander the farm lands around Berne. He took time off from the office. Mileva helped him solve certain mathematical problems, but nobody could assist with the creative work, the flow of fresh ideas.

Walking home from the office one night with Besso, who had some inkling of the problems, Einstein admitted that he had run up against a complete mental block. When he reached the steps to his apartment house, he paused briefly and said: "I've decided to give it up—the whole theory."

Perhaps because of the sudden relaxation after months of intense brain work, that night the missing pieces fell into place. Relativity yielded and came scrambling into the world. It was one of nature's most closely guarded secrets, something Man could not find under a microscope or hear or touch or smell. This had come from the inventive element of human reason that Kant had written about. Einstein had proved his creativity. He was ecstatic.

The transfer of the broad concept of the theory to its logical mathematical progression on paper took five weeks of sapping work. When it was over, Einstein's body buckled and he went to bed for two weeks. Mileva checked the article again and again, then mailed it. "It's a very beautiful piece of work," she told her husband.

Relativity first appeared in *Annalen der Physik* in the middle of 1905 as an article called "On the Electrodynamics of Bodies in Motion," a clean thirty pages not cluttered by footnote or reference. The frayed-cuff clerk of Berne had fashioned nothing less than a universe. Yet, as all creations by poor men working in garrets are slow to win glory, so at first did Einstein's theory of Relativity fail to stir the world.

Unintelligible nonsense, said scores of scientific readers of the physics journal. Sophistry, said others.

The Einstein theory presumed advanced knowledge of physics. More important, it presumed a state of mind, a certain abstraction. Max Planck and the few others who early appreciated the grandeur of Relativity made little attempt to publicize it. They decided it was beyond the reach of the average mind. It did not fit common thinking habits. Healthy skepticism was a lost quality in modern society. As one philosopher observed: "The trouble is that people are in the habit of taking things for granted when they have no right to do so." He said it might take generations for Relativity to "seep" into the public mind.

Einstein's article in the journal was noted by his academic

acquaintances in Berne, but they were not prepared to accept the word of a young patent officer as gospel on such momentous subjects. In the after-work coffee-house discussions, it was Einstein versus The Rest. They argued particularly about his simple statement that $E = MC^2$.

"You're saying there's more horsepower in a lump of coal than in the whole Prussian cavalry," they complained. "If this were true, why hasn't it been noticed before?"

"If a man who is fabulously rich never spent or gave away a cent," Einstein replied, "then no one could tell how rich he was or even whether he had any money at all. It is the same with matter. So long as none of the energy is given off externally, it cannot be observed."

"And how do you propose to release all this hidden energy?"

"There is not the slightest indication that the energy will ever be obtainable," said Einstein. "It would mean that the atom would have to be shattered at will. There is scarcely a sign that this will be possible. We see atom disintegration only where nature herself presents it, as in the case of radium. Radium's activity depends on the continual explosive decomposition of the atom."

The others wanted to know if Einstein had worked out his energy equation from radium experiments. To their horror, Einstein said he had not been inside a laboratory for years.

"Then this Relativity of yours is fiction," they said. "It is something you dreamed up. A proper physicist makes his discoveries by fresh experimentation and checking his results. That's the only way."

"Rubbish," said Einstein, the twenty-six-year-old civil

servant. "Physics is a logical system of thought in a state of evolution. Its basis cannot be obtained merely by experiment and experience. Its progress depends on free invention." He added, however, that Relativity must stand the test of human experience before it could be fully accepted. He smiled. "I haven't the faintest doubt that I am right."

Max Planck was the first major scientist to recognize Einstein's genius. The two men started a steady correspondence. Lorentz also wrote encouraging letters to the young man. But there was merely limited discussion about Relativity in science circles. Einstein toiled in his Berne obscurity for two years after his discovery. He was not upset; he liked his job. Actually, he was fiddling with mechanical gadgets himself, hoping to score a worthy invention. Mileva was secretly amused—Albert was hopeless at working with his hands.

In 1907 the directors of the University of Zurich finally noticed Einstein. They felt he showed promise so they offered him a position as *privatdozent*—an unpaid lecturer who would be promoted to an assistant physics professor if he proved his worth.

Einstein rejected the offer. But Dr. Heinrich Zangger, who headed the medical faculty at the University of Zurich and who had befriended Einstein soon after he left the Polytechnic, persuaded him to take a *privatdozent* role at the University of Berne. This would not interfere with his work at the Patent Office and, meanwhile, Zangger would try to get him an assistant professorship at Zurich.

Einstein agreed. He had no doubt that Zangger would get him the job in Zurich. In fact, he wondered if there was anything Zangger could not do. He was a tall, hawk-faced man with a brush mustache and deceptively dreamy eyes. Sometimes it was harrowing just to talk to him. He seemed to be adding up all the flaws in an argument while he looked around to see if a room had been dusted lately. He could recount any conversation exactly and at the same time mimic the attitudes of the speaker. Physicians often specialized in a particular branch of medicine. Zangger specialized in all branches. And when he read the Relativity article, he understood the whole thing without so much as stumbling over an equation.

But in spite of Zangger, the physics department at the University of Berne was cool to Einstein's application. Even when the young clerk was invited to two physics congresses in 1908 —one in Salzburg, Austria, and the other at Tivoli, near Rome —with all expenses paid, their enthusiasm was not aroused. Then word reached Berne that Einstein had walked the ruins of Tivoli for hours in deep consultation with the revered Lorentz, that Einstein had enthralled expert audiences with off-the-cuff lectures on his theories. The university grudgingly took him on.

It was also at this time that Hermann Minkowski, Einstein's old teacher, helped Relativity to wider acceptance by refining the new concept of time.

"From now on," said Minkowski, "space in itself and time in itself should descend into a shadow and only a union of both should retain its independence." Time became the fourth spatial co-ordinate in the determination of position—the fourth dimension.

Soon after this, when Minkowski was on his death bed, he

made a classic remark that revealed more about Einstein and the few other scientific seekers of truth-for-the-sake-of-truth than a dozen books.

"It's a pity," he said, "that I have to die in the era of the development of Relativity."

Only two men attended Einstein's first lecture during the winter of 1908–1909—his friend Besso and a young telegraph office assistant with an insatiable thirst for universal knowledge. Others drifted in as the semester progressed, but few stayed for long.

One night a physics professor from the University of Zurich, a man named Kleiner, came to study Einstein's style. Later Kleiner said it was no wonder nobody attended the lectures because Einstein was not *teaching* anything. He was merely chatting about various subjects that seemed to interest him personally. Even then he made mistakes and had to correct himself. Apparently he expected his listeners to become so intrigued that they would make their own independent detailed studies. This, said Kleiner, was not the accepted way to teach physics.

"I'll put it to you straight, Herr Einstein. As a lecturer, you're no damn good."

"That's all right," said Einstein. "I don't insist on being appointed to a professorship at Zurich."

Einstein was totally preoccupied during the summer of 1909 with extending Relativity into the realms of gravitation and with helping to change the diapers on his new-born second son, Edward. When Zangger told him he could have the job of assistant professor of theoretical physics in Zurich, Einstein was not overly excited. He suggested that since his friend, Friedrich Adler, was already a physics *privatdozent* at the University, he should be promoted first. Adler heard about this and urged the faculty committee to choose Einstein. In any case, Adler had other financial means and he was also busy pushing the cause of socialism.

Thus Einstein, reluctantly, returned to Zurich at the age of thirty. Off duty, he'd often be seen walking the streets, trundling a baby carriage with a book lying open on the blankets. If he got into what he called his "somnambulistic state," which he said was necessary for his intense thinking, he'd wander without direction and end up miles from home. Other times he would be in a gay, talkative mood. He'd stop and have a few words with the milk delivery boy or the president of the university—whoever happened along. In both conversations, his tone and manner would be identical.

Zangger came to the university badly shaken one day. He said he had gone to see Einstein at home, found the door unlocked, walked in, and discovered the professor pale and lifeless on the couch. All the windows were closed and the stove was hissing carbon monoxide fumes. Zangger threw open the window and held Einstein's head outside to revive him. Einstein explained that he had been deep in thought and must have dozed off.

The chemistry professor at the university, David Reichinstein, had another anecdote to tell of Einstein at home. Mrs. Einstein was out and Albert was looking after the children. "The door of the flat was open to allow the floor which had

51

just been scrubbed, as well as the washing hung up in the hall, to dry. I entered Einstein's room. He was calmly philosophic, with one hand rocking the bassinet in which there was a child. In his mouth Einstein had a bad, a very bad cigar, and in the other hand an open book. The stove was smoking horribly. How in the world could he bear it."

Reichinstein, a deeply intellectual man who considered Einstein another Socrates, found talks with his new friend most stimulating. But his mood of reverence was often broken by Einstein's repulsive smoking habits. He was hypnotized by the way Einstein moved a torn, wet cigar stub in his mouth. Once, the two were walking along a country lane and Einstein's cigar fell into the dust. The dark brown roll of tobacco soaked up the fine dust like a blotter. Einstein looked at it a second, seemed about to grind his heel into the butt, then changed his mind and picked it up. Dusting off the end with his finger, he stuffed it back into his mouth.

"Ahhh . . ." Reichinstein's groan was painful. "What about the germs?"

"I don't care a straw for germs," said Einstein.

Einstein did not care about any conventions at all. In Zurich, it was the fashion to dress to the spats for the theater. If the Einsteins went there from home, Mileva would make sure he was immaculate. But often he would come directly from the university and meet her at the theater. Then his suit would be crumpled and his thickly knotted tie would ride a good inch below his neck stud. Mileva would smuggle him a package of sandwiches for a quiet snack. He would never take the hint. At intermission he greeted friends with a mouth full of bread.

In spite of his eccentricities or perhaps because of them, the students were delighted with their new professor. Teaching in Zurich was a marked change from Berne, where he had lectured mainly at night and had had little contact with regular students. Now his lectures were crowded to the door. Einstein had developed a new style. He used his hands a great deal and threw in plenty of witticisms to build up the sympathy of his audience. He usually had one major point to make and he delivered it as dramatically as he could. Average students could never quite keep up with him, but the bright ones learned much from Einstein. They appreciated his respect for their intelligence. They knew he was trying to make them think for themselves rather than to hammer in formal knowledge. Einstein left the teaching of the set curriculum to the other professors.

In class he stayed off Relativity but obliged his friends by lecturing on it at Guild House, a local restaurant. By now, he was exchanging letters with some of the most renowned physicists in the world. Their acclaim gave him bursting confidence. He was aware of his talents without being conceited. Nature had given him the right gifts to become a creative man. Hard work had done the rest. Instead of growing pompous and sedate, recognition made him more jocular than ever.

At his first Guild House lecture, he spoke lengthily about the relativity of time. He put the notion of time through all sorts of hoops until everyone thought Einstein must be the high priest of time in a country famous for timepieces. An hour and more passed before he suddenly stopped, feigned anguish and said: "I fear it is getting late. Does anyone know

53

the time?"

After a year in Zurich, Einstein was offered a full professorship in experimental physics at the German University in Prague. It was tempting. The salary was nearly double the sixty dollars a month he was being paid in Zurich.

"But it's not your field," argued Mileva. "You're no good at experiments."

"No, you're right. I'll turn it down."

"It's a big break, Albert," a colleague told him. "You can't afford to pass up a full professorship."

"Of course not. I'll take it."

Einstein, as usual, was too involved with his private theoretical work to form an opinion on whether or not to uproot his family and move to Prague. But the decision was important to Mileva. She demanded that he make up his mind. Finally, he decided to give Prague a try.

After the move, the family could afford a large apartment and a maid who lived in. It was also their first flat with electricity. They had used kerosene lamps in Berne and gaslight in Zurich. These, however, were the only luxuries. Prague was a dismal place in which to live. Water from the faucets was brown and it left a black sediment in the basins. The Einsteins bought their drinking water in bottles and they lugged up their cooking water from fountains in the street. The city was full of beggars and disease. In 1910 bubonic plague and typhoid were not rare in Prague. And the fleas! Einstein never forgot the fleas. A fire broke out in the maid's room one night. Einstein rushed in with a bucket of water. He was there for only a few minutes but when he came out, he was crawling with fleas and had to take a bath.

Besides all this, Prague was a surly city. It was peopled mainly with Czechs, Germans and Jews, and each group was constantly insulting the other. To the irritation of the German professors, Einstein would not pick sides. He thought such bickering infantile. He stayed aloof, devoting all his time to his job and to his private research. Students enjoyed the sessions with Einstein in the physics laboratory. There was always an air of uncertainty; frequently his experiments did not work. His theoretical work, however, was dancing ahead.

He had imagined a man in a down elevator. Was he being accelerated down by mechanical power or was the elevator falling by the force of gravity? The effects on the man inside the closed elevator were identical in either case and he could never say with certainty what was happening. Einstein's intuition told him that here was a tremendous new piece of knowledge. Gravitation and acceleration caused the same effects. They were equivalent. Could he prove it? Experiments had shown that a sudden acceleration could throw a light beam off course. Gravity should do the same thing. Therefore, the path of light from a fixed star should veer slightly when it passed through the sun's gravitational field. This could be tested during an eclipse.

The theory seemed simple in précis. Many scientists would put it down as a flash of genius, but Mileva Einstein would bristle and complain, "Does nobody realize my husband works himself half to death? His passion to work, to know, always to know more—that's his genius."

Einstein had been puzzling over his latest creation for four years. While he had worked on it, he had turned out twenty-five other papers on physics problems, each of which was at least equal to a doctoral thesis. In Prague, he put the polish on his gravitation-acceleration theory and thought of the starlight test. It added up to only ten pages in *Annalen der Physik,* but there was an historic postscript at the end: "It would be extremely desirable if astronomers would look into the problem presented here, even though the consideration developed above may appear insufficiently founded and even bizarre."

Few in Prague had any notion of the extent of Einstein's obsession with physics. It even intruded into his music. He needed to play well-turned, complete pieces. He wanted harmony in his music as well as in the universe. To him, this meant Mozart. He played Mozart beautifully, and he played Mozart often.

On Tuesday evenings, some young Jewish intellectuals met at the Prague home of one Bertha Fanta to discuss philosophy. They invited Einstein. The German school of Kant, Fichte and Hegel was the usual topic of conversation. Einstein, who enjoyed any intellectual debate, joined in with zest. Frequently the discussion would turn to Zionism. The others were all ablaze over it. But Einstein was disinterested. He had no sympathy for patriotism, nationalism or racism in any form. He had not given the subject much thought because he felt it was a waste of time. His aloofness irritated the others. Some said he was devoid of the finer human emotions; he was keeping himself beyond the reach of the rest of the world for fear he would be tainted. They said he would not let his heart become a dominant factor in his life.

"He sought friends with whom he could play music or dis-cuss ideas about the universe," said Philipp Frank, the physicist and Einstein biographer who was to replace Einstein in Prague. "Yet he did not like to become so intimate with his friends that they could in any way interfere with his freedom. His attractive, frank and witty personality easily made friends, but his prediliction for isolation and his concentration on his artistic and scientific life disappointed many people and estranged some who had been, or at least believed themselves to be, his friends."

In November, 1911, Einstein was invited to a physics con-gress in Brussels, sponsored by the Belgian philanthropist, Ernest Solvay. It meant his acceptance into the elite among world scientists. Lorentz was in the chair, brilliant in his summation of debates and his perception of loose ends, casu-ally switching from Dutch to German to French as though this was his natural way of talking. "He's a miracle," Einstein at the time wrote to a friend, "a living work of art." Lorentz' "class" included Ernest Rutherford, Walther Nernst and Max Planck from Berlin, and Marie Curie, Paul Langevin, Jean Perrin and Henri Poincaré from Paris.

Newspapers reported the meeting, but they were more con-cerned with romance than physics. Paul Langevin, separated from his wife, was supposed to be courting Marie Curie and the Brussels meeting was named as their rendezvous. Madame Curie's husband, Pierre, had died five years before in a street accident. Einstein studied the legendary Madame Curie and wrote to Zangger: "She is sparklingly intelligent, but despite her passion she is not attractive enough to be really dangerous to anybody."

Einstein built a lasting friendship with Langevin and Madame Curie in Brussels. But he was particularly drawn to Lorentz and to Paul Ehrenfest, the eager, disheveled little Russian Jew he had met shortly before in Prague. The Russian was looking for work as a physics teacher. Now he had joined Lorentz at the University of Leyden in Holland.

Prague seemed desolate to Einstein after Brussels. It was too remote from the progressive centers of physics. His health was poor, too. He consulted Zangger who immediately diagnosed an allergy to the local water. He persuaded Einstein to return to Zurich to take up a professorship at his old school, the Polytechnic. The authorities there made the offer after they had checked Einstein's standing with Henri Poincaré. The Frenchman wrote: "In spite of his youth, Einstein already occupies a very honorable position among the prominent savants of our time."

Poincaré's fine reference, which was echoed in a letter from Madame Curie, meant more to the Zurich professors than Einstein's discoveries. He became highly fashionable—a man to befriend and to show off. Mileva could pick the phonies in a minute and Einstein relied on her judgment. Often she turned down invitations to parties because she felt the host wanted her husband there as a show-piece more than as a friend. Mileva also managed the family finances, saving a fair proportion of Albert's salary for the future or perhaps for buying

58

stock in some solid, growing company. She never speculated.

Close friends still regarded Mileva as the perfect wife for Albert, but they worried because her dark moods were becoming more frequent. She was far too introverted. She never talked about herself. Even alone with her family, she had little to say and her long periods of silence irritated Albert. If they ever discussed the root of the trouble, that mysterious pre-marital incident, nobody knew about it.

Hans Albert, then an eight-year-old with a distinct mind of his own, sensed the tension between his parents. But his father's personality reassured him that all would be well.

Einstein fairly brimmed over with life. Like a child, he liked to sneak extra time in bed in the morning. Mileva would finally get him out. He whistled merrily while he shaved and dressed. He ate breakfast hungrily and walked off to the university, twenty minutes away, with a jaunty stride. In the late afternoon, before dinner, he spent time with his sons. He liked to play with their toys. He loved to play his violin while Hans Albert played a little tune on the piano. Edward was only three then and just starting to plunk the piano. His father said it would not be long before "Teddy" was playing too. At three, Edward was already reading. Sometimes the boys were naughty and Einstein spanked them. But he could not stay angry. He preferred to laugh. Hans Albert thought his father was "a riot." But not when he was working. He hated to be interrupted when he worked.

Gravity: a force—or a field? He advanced his new concept as far as he could, and then his mathematics failed him. The problem was too complex for Mileva. He called on Marcel

Grossman who had made mathematics his career. "Help me, Marcel, or I'll go crazy." Grossman came, and together they made more progress.

Grossman was a good friend. So, too, were Zangger, Besso, Adler and Reichinstein. They liked Albert for himself and they understood Mileva. Close by, in Lucerne, lived Albert's sister Maja. Her husband, Paul, had a good job as a railroad lawyer. They had brought the widowed Pauline Einstein from Italy to live with them.

Those were good days and everybody was content and prosperous. The strife and hatred in other parts of Europe were far away. Mileva wanted this happy time to last forever. She was conscious of her brooding, but one day it would pass. The occasional squabbles with Albert were not all her fault. He had not changed basically since college. He was still infuriatingly vague about worldly matters. He could also be stubborn. If he reasoned something out to the last detail and made up his mind one way or the other, nobody could budge him. Take psychoanalysis, for instance. Albert had decided this was worth investigating. He studied it, reasoned it, and found it too inconclusive. After that, he refused to take it seriously. Zangger argued the point. Albert wouldn't change. This was only one example. Perhaps it was not vital, but it did make people cross.

Mileva pondered her man, recognized his faults and accepted them. It was, all things considered, a good marriage.

Towards the end of 1913, Walther Nernst and Max Planck came down from Berlin to offer Einstein a position with the Prussian Academy of Sciences. He would be paid a generous salary simply to investigate. He need lecture at the University of Berlin only when he felt like it. Later, he would head the physics department at the Kaiser Wilhelm Physical Institute. This was still in the planning stage.

It was a fantastic offer for a thirty-four-year-old physicist. Appointment to the academy was considered the highest scientific honor in Europe. Einstein did not know what to say. His gravitational theory was the most important thing in his life and he had been worried that he would not find enough time to spend on it in Zurich. On the other hand, there was the drawback of living in the Prussian capital. He asked Nernst and Planck for time to think the offer over.

Mileva was strongly against the idea. But Einstein said this was one decision he would make alone. He had a doubt at the back of his mind. Perhaps his creative drive had stopped. "These Berlin people are speculating with me as if I were a prize hen," he said. "But I don't know whether I can still lay eggs."

However, from the start, his friends knew Einstein would accept. After all, this was his dream—nothing to do but think and make calculations all day. Mileva was dejected but not surprised when Albert announced his decision.

CHAPTER 4

THE WORLD AT WAR

The Einstein family arrived in Berlin in April, 1914, and rented an apartment in the suburb of Dahlem. Mileva went about her housekeeping gloomily. She did not have any friends in Berlin. She hated the city at first sight. Edward stayed home with her. He was an extraordinary child. At five he had started reading Shakespeare. Hans Albert went to a local school and complained from the start about the rigid discipline and the method of teaching. "They teach only one thing," he said. "They teach you how to memorize."

Albert alone warmed to his new surroundings. He had a cool office at the academy, which was housed in the Prussian State Library opposite the monument of Frederick the Great on Unter den Linden. He lunched most days with celebrated scientists like Planck, Gustav Hertz, Max von Laue and Lise Meitner. There were regular seminars at which the latest discoveries in science were discussed in detail. Einstein was able to devote nearly all his time to gravitation. He lectured spasmodically at the university. Noticing several very promising students, he invited them to come to him with their problems at any time. "I can turn off my own research like a tap," he lied.

The same petty jealousies and intrigues existed among the Berlin professors as in Zurich or Prague, but they soon learned that Einstein had no time for gossip. European politics was also a major interest of theirs. Again, Einstein took no part. He had worried about the nationalistic atmosphere in Berlin and had insisted on preserving his Swiss citizenship so that he could keep neutral. However, he could not remain completely blind to politics.

Although there was no sound of gunfire in Europe and most countries seemed prosperous and hopeful of settling all disputes with diplomacy, there was a rumble of serious trouble ahead. Many nations were building up arms "just in case." Historically, such stockpiles get used. Where to use these? The obvious war danger existed in the bitter feud over territories between Austria and Serbia. European nations were picking sides in the squabble and nobody was looking ahead to the day of climax. It would be a big explosion because Germany was behind Austria and Russia backed Serbia.

Einstein was aware of this slow-burning fuse, but he hoped it would be snuffed out in time. He convinced himself that his work would be undisturbed, even in Berlin.

When the schools broke for the 1914 summer, Mileva took the boys back to Zurich for a vacation. Einstein went with them to the station and kissed his wife goodbye. The family would return in September.

But Einstein's life and that of the world changed in one hot week, July 28 to August 3. Austria declared war on Serbia. Russia mobilized to support Serbia, but kept talking to Austria to avert disaster. Germany ordered Russia to end her military "provocation" or risk war. There was no reply, so Germany declared war on Russia and, two days later, on France. Why not? reasoned the German generals. France would join Russia in any case. And the Germans had seven great invincible armies totaling 1,500,000 men. They were armed to the teeth and ready to move.

Move they did on the night of August 4—right across the frontier of neutral Belgium. England then denounced the barbaric invasion and declared war on Germany. World War I was on. From the flash fire in the south, Germany lit the torch to put all Europe in flames.

In Berlin, Einstein was horrified. One of his first thoughts was for his friend, Professor Erwin Freundlich of the Potsdam Observatory, who had gone to Russia to study a sun eclipse and test Einstein's theory of bending light. He would be thrown into a prisoner-of-war camp.

Einstein blamed the Prussian generals for the magnitude of the war. As the days passed and Von Kluck's soldiers butchered their way towards Brussels, he could not resist voicing his disgust at the academy lunch table. His companions were compassionate men and he looked for some support. He received only frowns. Planck, Nernst, Röntgen, the X-ray man, and several of the others were fine scientists, but they had one blind spot—Prussianism. This showed Einstein how extreme patriotism can twist reason. Reminding himself that he was neutral in this madness, he got back to his studies, promising himself to keep his mouth shut. But privately in a letter to Paul Ehrenfest he grumbled, "It is difficult to reconcile one-self to the fact that one belongs to that idiotic, rotten species which boasts of its freedom of will."

A document entitled "Manifesto to the Civilized World" was circulated among the scientists, philosophers, writers, musicians and artists at the academy and at Berlin University. It said that Germany had to go to war to avert her own de-struction . . . that German militarism and German culture were interwoven . . . that Germany was actually safeguard-ing modern civilization. Most of the people at the academy signed the paper. But Einstein read it and laughed.

Soon after, he was sitting beside the novelist, Hermann Sudermann, at a seminar. He knew Sudermann casually and respected him as a fine talent and a pleasant man. Einstein nudged him and asked if he had seen the manifesto. "Hah, it's an epic," said Einstein, "an epic in lunacy." Sudermann smiled and replied blandly that he was the author. Einstein gaped. Sudermann was obviously quite happy about his creation.

In spite of this, Einstein's relationship with men like Suder-mann remained cordial. He regarded their nationalism as a deep-sown sickness they could not control. They would have to be educated, rather than jolted out of it.

At the time one of his fellow musicians at the academy was Fritz Haber, the great chemist. Haber, together with Nernst, now started secret investigations into poisonous gases on assignment from the army and both received commissions as majors. Haber, to Einstein's bewilderment, was extremely proud of his new status.

Einstein alone refused war work. He was well aware of how his friends were violating their talents. One day a Berlin newspaper complained that the Allies were not fighting fair. They were using dumdum bullets and gas bombs. Einstein slapped the paper and snorted to a friend: "This is supposed to mean that they stunk first. I know better." Haber had given him details of Germany's deadly gas bombs.

When another edict was circulated around the academy ordering German physicists not to mention the work of English physicists in their papers, Einstein lost his temper. He would not idly watch the sabotage of the traditional internationalism of science. He and Georg Nicolai, the physiology professor at Berlin University and an outspoken pacifist, drew up an opposing document calling on intellectuals to join forces in demanding a just peace and to work towards the creation of a united Europe. Of the one hundred men asked to sign the manifesto, only three or four agreed. Nicolai, who did most of the campaigning, charged bluntly that they were too cowardly.

Nicolai risked personal ruin in speaking out as he did. Einstein knew this and was impressed. He even felt a little overshadowed by Nicolai—not as a scientist but as a man. He would have accepted criticism from this friend about his enforced detachment, but Nicolai said Einstein's position as a "latter-day Archimedes" justified his neutral stand. Nevertheless, Einstein remained troubled. He was moved to join the liberal New Fatherland League devoted to the cause of outlawing war. Nicolai insisted such a group was important in rallying men of fine international principles "hiding presently in lonely corners." Einstein on the other hand, felt the task was almost hopeless.

He became intolerant of the German people generally. He was sickened at the joy in the streets when a new military victory was announced. He found the people greedy and savage.

The war had prevented Mileva's return to Berlin. She implored Albert to come back to Zurich himself. He wrote that the war was not affecting his work. It was going very well and he did not want to interrupt it now. In Zurich, he would have to find a job and this would set him back. But he urged Mileva to stay in Switzerland. "I want our sons educated in Swiss schools," he said. Albert did not mention when the family might get together again. Mileva knew that was typical of him. While his mind was on his work, nothing else counted. He would think about his family "later."

It was a year later, when Einstein hit a snag in his research, that he went to Switzerland to visit Mileva and the boys. He took Hans Albert on a long walking tour, right up into southern Germany. They stayed at little, out-of-the-way inns. They went boating on the Danube. The boy asked his father if they were going back to Germany with him. "I want you educated in Switzerland," he repeated and then changed the subject. They had a great time on their trek and when it was over, Einstein seemed strangely sad.

Back in Zurich, Mileva tried to get a straight answer from her husband about the future. It was useless.

Before he returned to Berlin, Einstein sought out the French writer and pacifist, Romain Rolland, then in voluntary exile at the Hotel Mooser in the Swiss town of Vevey. Einstein told Rolland that his cause had some supporters in Berlin. He would happily do anything he could to help. In mock conspiratorial tone, he offered his services as a "drop" for pacifist literature.

Even on serious matters, Einstein's humor bubbled up. He told Rolland how comical he found a weekly meeting at a Berlin beer-house where members of his academy gathered to debate the question of why Germany was so hated by the rest of the world.

Rolland gave him several copies of his new book, *Au-dessus de la Mêlée* (*Above the Battle*), which explained his pacifist philosophy. Rolland talked seriously. Einstein watched him closely. Again, he was face to face with a man who had faith in the ability of a few dedicated men to kindle an altruistic spirit that would change the world. He wanted to be convinced they were right. But his perspective got in the way. It seemed to him that young Germans of the twentieth century had two major life philosophies set before them by their countrymen: that of the universalist Goethe and that of the glorified German historian, Heinrich von Treitschke who preached the divinity of the Prussian State and the destiny of Prussians to triumph over all men. The fact that the young generation chose Treitschke was to him "an immeasurably sad thing."

After Einstein had left, Rolland recorded this description of the thirty-six-year-old physicist in his diary: "Einstein is still a young man, not very tall, with a wide and long face, and a great mane of crisp, frizzled and very black hair, sprinkled with gray and rising from a lofty brow. His nose is fleshy and prominent, his mouth small, his lips full, his cheeks plump, his chin rounded. He wears a small cropped mustache."

A steady supply of pacifist pamphlets and books reached Einstein from Switzerland and Holland, and he was able to smuggle some to fellow heretics who had been imprisoned. For this, he used a committee of Swiss citizens, set up to help foreigners stranded in Berlin by the war, which had access to jails. Some committee members objected to risks involved in smuggling, but Einstein was unmoved.

"He seemed to make an almost gleeful game of circumventing the authorities," recalled Franziska Tramer, one of the members. "He chortled every time he learned that he had succeeded in getting letters or books into a prison."

Einstein might have done more, but, towards the end of 1915, he was fully captive in his world of physics. The extension of Relativity to gravitation had been held up because of his shortcomings in mathematics—his neglected subject at college. But suddenly he had perceived a new way to advance. He found the key in a "curved" geometry worked out sixty years before by the German mathematician, Georg Riemann. Einstein used this to solve field equations that would give the geometry of the "warp" in space created by a moving body and also the path of another body intruding into the distorted area. He tried his new equations on the known traveling habits of the planet Mercury. Astronomers had been puzzled by Mercury because it defied Newton's gravitational theory by a slight "drift" in its orbit. Einstein's equations explained the eccentricity. They also gave him an exact measurement by which starlight would be deflected by the sun.

The perfecting of the general theory of Relativity took about the same time as the Allies spent in a bloody and futile attempt to capture Gallipoli. Einstein knew which of the two events would live longer in history. He was thrilled. To a physicist friend in Munich who had chided him for not replying to letters, Einstein wrote: "I have just experienced one of the most exciting and most exacting times of my life, also one of the most successful. Letter-writing was out of the question."

Einstein's joy over his new advance in Relativity lasted him a long time and kept him immune from worries about the savagery of the world. He was spurred to new investigations and he was producing many articles for various physics journals.

But his wary cheerfulness turned to gloom on October 21, 1916. A news flash said that the Austrian prime minister, Count Karl von Sturgkh, had been assassinated. The murderer was Friedrich Adler. Einstein thought of his years in Zurich with Adler. They had lived in the same apartment house for a time. Adler had bought one of the first typewriters made. He treated it like a baby, but once he had let Hans Albert try it out. The boy had never forgotten this.

Nicolai, Rolland, Adler—men of intellectual and physical daring, ready to die for justice on earth. It was a life-consuming task. Einstein's own life and job was science. Yet these men were his true compatriots on earth and he must not let them fight alone. He sat down and wrote an appreciation of Adler as a physicist for publication in a science journal. This was his only sphere of influence. His by-line was well known. In some way it might help his friend.

Now there was a letter from Mileva. Her brother Milosh, a medical officer in the Austrian army, had been captured by the Russians. Heartbreaks followed one after the other. This was the time of the Battle of the Somme. More than a million men were killed or wounded. Germany made a few insincere peace overtures. Far from wanting peace, the German people seemed furious at the high command for not letting German submarines out on patrol. Many felt this was the sure way to a quick victory. Submarine warfare had been restricted since early 1916 because America threatened action if any more of her ships were torpedoed.

On January 31, 1917, Germany told the United States that unrestricted submarine attacks would resume. Two months later, the United States declared war on Germany.

"The ancient Jehovah is still abroad," Einstein said in a letter to Ehrenfest. "Alas, he slays the innocent along with the guilty, whom he strikes so fearsomely blind that they can feel no sense of guilt . . . We are dealing with an epidemic delusion. It will cause infinite suffering and then one day vanish to become a monstrous and incomprehensible source of wonderment to a later generation."

Ehrenfest detected a certain drag to Einstein's small, firm handwriting. The usual flourish to the R's and N's was missing. He heard later that Einstein was depressed and sick with stomach trouble. Doctors could not make up their minds whether he had ulcers or an inflammation of the gall bladder.

By this time, Einstein had taken a bachelor flat just around the corner from an apartment rented by Rudolph Einstein, his late father's cousin. Rudolph's daughter Elsa, a thick and jolly woman five years older than Albert, was living there with her two young daughters. Her husband had died. Albert had first met Elsa when he was a boy in Munich. They had exchanged a few letters over the years. Actually they had little in common. Elsa was a typical *hausfrau,* devoted to her family and with no intellectual pretensions at all. She had very weak eyesight and had to hold a newspaper close to her eyes to read it. Like many people with this trouble, she was careless about her appearance. Albert did not notice. Elsa was kind and gentle and an excellent cook. And right then he wanted comfort, not romance.

When Albert's stomach trouble worsened and he needed constant nursing, he moved into Elsa's flat. Rudolph was not living there then, but Albert did not think of any possible scandal. He was in bed, often in agony, for weeks. Friends thought he might die. Elsa stayed at his bedside, soothing him and plying him with medicine and soup. He lost more than fifty pounds, but slowly he started to respond to treatment. By late 1917, he was well again and was able to resume his duties at the academy.

However, he never did return to his bachelor flat. He stayed on with Elsa and her two daughters. He did not bother to explain to gossipers that he had his own bedroom, even ate many of his meals alone.

Mileva heard of her husband's new quarters and was not pleased. She had never given up hope that she and Albert would get together again. She was still in love with him. But now he must decide about his future with his family. Zangger interceded and urged Einstein not to make a final split with

Mileva. He reminded him that the two boys must be considered.

It was an agonizing dilemma for Einstein. And in the end his heart decided. His obsession for his work transcended his love for his wife and sons. He had no control over it. As a boy he had resolved to spend his life searching for knowledge, truth. The resolve had been unnecessary. He had been born with it. His every fiber was now attuned to his work. It was his reason for being alive. He was nearing forty—slowing down. He had a great deal left to accomplish and he must give himself every chance. He was free in Berlin and the atmosphere at the academy was stimulating to his mind. Einstein knew he was not like other men. Few understood how a man's heart could be divided between human love and apparently abstract science. With him, the science was dominant.

He wrote to Mileva and told her to divorce him. He explained his position and at the end of the letter, he added a poignant, enigmatic note, "You will see that I will always remain true to you—in my way."

The boys had sensed their father was not coming back to them. They were not surprised when their mother told them she was going ahead with the divorce. The grounds would be "incompatibility of humor." Einstein need not appear in court. He could be represented by a lawyer.

Friends looked at Mileva for a sign of bitterness. There was none. She understood her husband better than anyone alive. Her only resentment was against Elsa. She had met her before and did not like her. But she knew Albert would not rely on her instinct this time.

An associate visiting Haberlandstrasse said Einstein was "like a Bohemian guest in a middle-class home," but the man himself was in condition to roam the universe and he was content. He remained oblivious to the snide remarks made at the academy about Elsa's intellect. He did not notice the stunned look in the eyes of visitors when Elsa patted him and admonished him as if he were a small boy. Einstein did not satisfy their notion of a great physicist at home.

Biedermeier furniture, heavy and dark, dominated the living room. The flowered yellow wallpaper was adorned only with a few family pictures in thick frames and, for some reason or other, a portrait of Frederick the Great with two dogs at heel. Buff busts of Schiller and Goethe stared blindly from two pedestals. A squat piano, with three violin cases underneath, stood by the window. Every morning Einstein sat at the piano and improvised little fantasies for his own pleasure. Elsa learned that this was as important to Albert as eating and much more personal. She stayed out of the room while he played.

In the library, a wall-to-ceiling bookcase relieved the oppression of green wallpaper. It was jammed with novels and books on science, history and philosophy. On the lower shelves, at armchair level, were Shakespeare, Dostoevski, Homer, Cervantes, Strindberg, Schopenhauer, Spinoza, Zola and two huge copies of the Bible. Einstein was reading more and more. He could never satisfy his appetite for learning.

He established a private domain in the attic atop the apartment house. Sometimes he closeted himself inside this room for three days at a stretch. Elsa would leave his meals at the door on a tray.

Einstein's bedroom was monkish. There were no pictures on the wall, no carpet on the floor. His bed was topped with a tucked-in gray blanket.

"Every possession is a stone around the leg," he told a friend of Elsa's who once had the cheerless experience of using his bedroom while he was away. "There is nothing that I could not dispense with at any moment."

He started to lead a Spartan life. He shaved roughly with bar soap. He often went barefoot around the house. Only once every few months would he allow Elsa to lop off swatches of his hair with scissors.

Alice Steinhardt, his cousin, remembered boarding a train with Elsa and Albert one cold day in Berlin. Einstein was shivering. Elsa looked at him a second, then reached forward and poked a finger through the opening of his jacket. "Ach, you've forgotten to put on your underwear," she scolded.

Most days he did not find underwear necessary. He also dispensed with pajamas and, later, with socks. "What use are socks?" he asked. "They only produce holes." Elsa put her foot down when she saw him chopping off the sleeves of a new shirt from the elbow down. He explained that cuffs had to be buttoned or studded and washed frequently—all a waste of time.

Elsa's non-scientific friends thought he was weird. At the dinner table, he was dreamy, his mind far away. After coffee, he might get up suddenly and take his violin to the kitchen to play.

"What brought this on?" they would ask.

"The acoustics are better in here," he would reply, not getting the point.

He could not bear to lose time on small talk. With his own friends, he even gave up saying hello, preferring to plunge right into a conversation. He was eager to talk about new ideas in science and philosophy. His arguments were succinct, profound and unpredictable. Often a friend so cherished an "Einsteinism" that he treated it as a private treasure and refused to share it.

Hedwig Born, the gentle wife of the brilliant physicist Max Born, used to talk over her troubles with Einstein. She was a Quaker and the war sickened her. "His serenity gave me peace of mind," she said.

Once she asked him if he feared death. He talked of eternity, the continuity of mankind, and added: "It does not matter to me where a single life starts and stops." Hedwig Born was troubled because scientists seemed determined to reduce the mystery of the universe to a few cold equations. "It's conceivable they will," laughed Einstein. "But don't worry. It would be forever inadequate—something like representing a Beethoven symphony by air pressure curves."

He had not lost his taste for laughter. Alexander Moszkowski, a noted Berlin critic and philosopher who came to the house often during the war, once bet Einstein he could not take off his waistcoat without first removing his coat. Einstein dressed up in his one good suit and tied himself in knots trying to do the trick. He finally succeeded and held his torn and crumpled waistcoat aloft, shaking with uncontrolled laughter.

Another time, he had Moszkowski and other friends roaring with laughter in a solid hour of joke-telling. He told them one after the other. Afterwards, he sheepishly produced his source—a well-thumbed copy of a book called *The One Hundred Best Jewish Jokes*.

Einstein was taking more notice of the outside world now in spite of himself. He had a small guilt feeling that he should be doing or saying something to hasten the peace. His friend Nicolai had been dishonored and made to work as an orderly in a field hospital. Adler's death sentence had been commuted but he still faced life imprisonment. Einstein was half-convinced that their fight for idealism and liberalism would never get anywhere in Germany. The German people respected nothing but force. So he wanted the Allies to win the war and use economic sanctions to force Germany to fall into line and live equitably with other nations.

In November, 1917, the Bolsheviks revolted in Petrograd, seized the Winter Palace and took over the government. They sold out Poland and the Ukraine for a quick peace with Germany and mobilized for civil war. Now the world would be split in three.

"Ah, the tragedy of it all," said Einstein. "It no longer even helps to escape into physics."

But, as always, he was able to shut out the world scene as soon as he conceived a new idea and started developing it. All through 1918, he worked hard and well. More than a dozen new theses came from his garret hideaway.

While he toiled, Europe fought on. Heavy military losses through the bitter summer and fall campaigns, coupled with the collapse of Bulgaria, brought fear and unrest to Germany. In early November, German sailors mutinied; people rioted in the streets of Munich; and pressure in Berlin forced the Kaiser to abdicate. The German Republic was proclaimed and its liberal and socialist leaders agreed to an armistice on Allied terms.

"The great event has happened," Einstein said in a letter to his mother in Lucerne. "Militarism and bureaucracy have been thoroughly abolished here . . . I am very happy at the way things are developing. Only now do I begin to feel at ease . . ."

His mood did not last.

Einstein agreed with President Woodrow Wilson of the United States that the time was right to start building the world anew. True democracies must be established in every country. Imperialism must end. A multi-nation body must be empowered to keep world peace and see justice done in all international affairs. Germany must be disarmed, made to pay reasonable reparations, deprived of its overseas territories.

The Treaty of Versailles did provide for the League of Nations. This was its only concession to Wilson and idealism. Einstein thought the rest of the treaty was designed to bleed Germany dry. It was a document of revenge, he said. Germany was left without dignity and without hope of aspiring to a new prosperity in the democratic fashion.

Already in Germany there was hunger, unemployment, inflation and sickness. Resentment at the treaty was fierce. Within the new democratic government, reactionaries of the right and left kept the resentment alive.

But Einstein had only one eye on these proceedings. Relativity, he said, once more passionately absorbed him day and night. He had heard from Lorentz about the British expeditions to test his starlight predictions and he anxiously awaited results. He had no thoughts for anything else.

Elsa came to him then and said they should be married. His divorce had come through months before. He was a free man. Elsa said she feared gossip about their living together would embarrass her daughters. Personally she didn't care and she knew he didn't mind. But they had to consider Ilse and Margot.

"Whatever you think best," said Einstein. So, in the summer of 1919, they went together to a registry office in Berlin and were married.

Afterwards he caught the train to Switzerland. He visited Mileva and his sons in Zurich to tell them about his marriage to Elsa. It was an unhappy meeting. Mileva hardly said a word. Hans Albert was hostile to his father. Now a husky boy of fifteen and fiercely independent, he told his father he had definitely made up his mind to become an engineer, although he knew that Einstein wanted him to follow a more "purely scientific" career.

"I think it's a disgusting idea," Einstein said.

"I'm still going to an engineer," the boy insisted.

Einstein strode away saying that he never wanted to see his older son again. Mileva waited until he had cooled down and later brought the two together again. She kept telling both boys that Einstein was still their father and wanted their love and respect. He was a strange man in many ways, she explained, but he *was* good and kind. Mileva knew that for all his bluff, Albert could be hurt in personal matters—and hurt deeply.

It was late September before Einstein returned to Berlin. There was still no news about the British starlight tests. He waited a week. Then he sent his letter to Ehrenfest: "Have you by chance heard anything about the British eclipse expedition?"

Six weeks later the whole world had heard about it.

CHAPTER 5

EINSTEIN FOR THE PEOPLE

The sudden arrival of fame put Albert Einstein in an odd predicament. Pacifist and liberal groups in Europe solicited his public support for a variety of causes. They wanted as many world figures as they could get on their side—and Einstein was the new giant.

He was reluctant to become too involved. He had left his family to devote all his time and emotion to his work. Yet he realized fame gave him influence, and his duty to humanity was to put it to some use. He had fervently hoped that peace would bring a new era of harmony on earth, but things were not working out that way. Chauvinists were still running the world. There was an urgent need to spread idealism. Everybody who felt this need keenly enough should help.

"My passionate sense of social justice and social responsibility has always contrasted oddly with my pronounced lack of need for direct contact with other human beings," Einstein said, in a frank assessment of his feelings. "By nature, I am a lone traveler. I have never belonged to my country, my home, my friends, or even my immediate family with my whole heart."

The world was passing through the greatest transition in history. Russia was torn apart in the bloody experiment of Communism. Central Europe was desolate and confused as autocratic forces tried to seize power in some places and Democracy attempted to root in others. In Einstein's home city of Berlin, nobody could say who would control the Reichstag a month hence—the Bolsheviks, the Fascists or the Democrats. A vicious economic circle was squeezing the life out of several countries. Lack of coal made factories idle. Without exports, countries like Austria and Czechoslovakia could not buy food or fuel. Poland had coal and Yugoslavia had food, but they sold these treasures for francs, dollars and sterling to buy raw materials to restart their industries. It was feared that five million people would die of cold and hunger in the winter of 1919–1920 unless mercy came by the trainload.

The machinery of peace had broken down. None of the treaties negotiated in Paris had been promulgated. The United States Senate refused to ratify the Treaty of Versailles. Isolationists blocked the issue. They wanted no part of Europe's troubles. Gustav Noske fumed in Berlin: "The Americans, after having helped destroy us, are now watching the proceedings with their hands in their trouser pockets." The American author and correspondent, Isaac Marcosson, returned to New York at the end of 1919 after a long tour of Europe and accused the senators of "knocking the props out from under a cripple and refusing him succor."

America's dilemma was parallel to Einstein's. To get involved or not to get involved. The American senators decided to stay out. Einstein began to attack what he saw as the underlying world evil—nationalism. He called it a disease—"the measles of mankind." In a growing swell of public statements, he denounced it from all sides and in all ways. He wanted to educate people to the universal view of life so they would see the pettiness of emotions like envy, hate and greed. He hoped they would see that avid nationalism encouraged these emotions. The way to lasting peace, he said, was to lower national frontiers, to unite under a world council of nations. Einstein varied his approach, using both the club and the pinprick.

The Times of London asked him for a simple explanation of his theories and for a short biographical note. He considered the second request wryly for a moment and then wrote: "Today I am described in Germany as a German savant and in England as a Swiss Jew. Should it ever become my fate to be represented as a bête noire, I should, on the contrary, become a Swiss Jew for the Germans and a German savant for the English."

The barb went deeply. Many people in England said petulantly that Einstein should stick to his physics and leave comedy to others. In Berlin, he was accused of denying his German nationality. Einstein replied that he had never concealed that he was born in Germany to German Jewish parents and had later become a Swiss by immigration. He was still a Swiss citizen.

Nationalist German were infuriated by this flat pronouncement. At first they had welcomed Einstein as a desperately needed boost to the world prestige of the defeated Fatherland. It takes Berlin to produce a real scholar, they had said. It had proved again that Germans were the superior race. The myth toppled with Einstein's shout that he was a Jew, a foreigner, a non-Aryan. He seemed to infer that he had succeeded despite the influence of Germany. Chauvinistic newspapers in Berlin started a smear campaign. They told the "miserable little Jew" to go home to Switzerland.

Einstein would not be silenced. On the raw, windy night of December 16, 1919, he shouldered his way through a gang of pickets outside a hall where the Bund Neues Vaterland (New Fatherland League) was conducting a meeting. The league was a pacifist group with the ideal of a United States of Europe. Einstein had been an enthusiastic member all through the war. This night he was called on for a speech and he spoke solemnly . . . "The hour is grave and the tasks before us are stern. Nationalist passions have been fanned into flame. The root of the evil is . . . the traditions which have been handed down by the educated classes in Europe from generation to generation, traditions which defy the Christian morality to which they pay lip service: he who commits rape and oppression will enjoy honor and glory, but he who experiences injustice will suffer shame and ignominy. These ancient and evil traditions threaten to seal the doom of our continent. We will oppose them with our passionate belief in the brotherhood of all men."

At the gray dawn of 1920 it seemed Einstein faced an impossible crusade. *Berliner Tageblatt,* Germany's best liberal newspaper and the only one Einstein read regularly every morning, urged the nation to make Carlyle's words its motto for the New Year: "Work and doubt not." But the many ultra-conservative papers would not look ahead. They fretted over 1919, "the blackest and most disastrous year in German history," and accused the Allies of enslaving their country.

"Happy New Year," said one sour editorial. "We can look forward to dearer bread, higher train fares, increased taxes, more expensive gas, coal and electricity." Broken in body and spirit, the people lacked the zest for work. Mercilessly a savage new disease called Spanish flu raged in the land. Hospital beds and corridors were filled. Medicines could be bought only on the black market. Profiteers waxed fat in the hotels of Berlin while people died in the streets. One night such a group sat over a meal of beef and wine with wealthy fugitives from the Russian Revolution—trading for diamonds and sables and rare china pieces. Less than a mile away a man shot his wife and three children and then himself because he was out of his mind with tears and hunger. Further across town, Einstein sat at the table in his garret and wrote to Ehrenfest: "Suffering is dreadful here . . . Where are we headed? . . . The government has sunk into utter impotence."

Political unrest mounted in January and February and erupted in violence in March. A reactionary *coup d'état,* supported by Junker officers and other rightist groups led by Dr. Wolfgang Kapp, seized control in Berlin. But within a week the rebels were driven out by a general strike and by troops sent in by the Ebert Government which had set up operations in Stuttgart. Communist rabble made a move in the same month. They organized armed uprisings at Essen and in cities to the south. Martial law was proclaimed and again an uneasy quiet was restored.

Nationalists sought for the cause of the unceasing woes of the Fatherland. Inevitably, they blamed the Jews. A great tide of anti-Semitism swept over the country. Jewish storekeepers were beaten up and their store windows smashed. Jewish children were spat at and kicked to one side on the street. Profiteers and smugglers were labeled as "Jew pigs." Bolshevism was "exposed" as a Jewish movement. "Trotsky and his Jews plot to break down Christianity and impose Jewish dictatorship throughout the world," said the propaganda sheets.

Einstein was given special attention. Rightist newspapers implied that he had some foul plot to discredit German science with his "stupid Relativity." They found scientists of intense patriotism who, in letters and articles, decried Relativity as "Bolshevism in physics" and "Jewish mathematics." The charges seemed odd in the light of a Moscow denouncement that Relativity was "a product of the bourgeois class in decomposition," but the newspaper attacks did not lessen. They became a mainstream in the flood of anti-Semitic literature.

Insults were hurled at Einstein by people who waited in front of his house on Haberlandstrasse or by the offices of the Prussian Academy of Sciences on Unter den Linden. Threatening letters appeared in his mail box. But he was not moved to any kind of fear or stealth. When Jewish students came to him, complaining that they had been refused admittance to the University of Berlin and other colleges in Europe, he initiated special lectures for them.

Many Jews in Berlin were annoyed at Einstein. Their only desire was to assimilate quietly into the local citizenry. They were not interested in causes. Einstein alienated them more when he joined the Zionists. He was recruited by Kurt Blumenfeld, a Zionist leader in Berlin. Blumenfeld did not try to talk Einstein into Zionism. He merely submitted facts and suggestions—anything, he said, to feed Einstein's "latent Jewish soul"—and waited for the physicist to convince himself that the cause was worthwhile. The strategy worked.

Judaism had played little part in Einstein's life up to this time. Religion had never been an issue during his marriage to Mileva. She was Greek Orthodox but did not go to church. His sons were not being brought up in any faith and did not count themselves as Jews. Now, however, Einstein was more aware of his heritage. Judaism was a race as well as a religion, and he was proud of the democratic, intellectual tradition of the Jews. He insisted that as a snail can shed his shell and still be a snail, so can a Jew shed his faith and still be a Jew.

Einstein supported Zionism because he felt a national home was needed for the Jews to preserve and build their idealism. It was also needed as a refuge. "I realized that salvation was only possible for the race if every Jew in the world should become attached to a living society to which he, as an individual, might rejoice to belong, and which might enable him to bear the hatred and humiliations which he has to put up with from the rest of the world," he said.

Einstein's name was constantly in the newspapers. He was accused of seeking publicity so as to advertise Relativity. His enemies said his position at the academy should be "reviewed."

Max Planck, Max von Laue and a few others publicly vouched for Einstein's integrity. But it made little difference.

A big weekly magazine said in an editorial: "One cannot blame workers for being taken in by Marx, when German professors allow themselves to be misled by Einstein. We are dealing here with an infamous scientific scandal." An anti-Semite leader named Rudolph Leibus was arrested because of offering a reward for Einstein's murder. Leibus was fined sixteen dollars and released. A group of black-shirted students broke up one of Einstein's lectures at the University of Berlin. A blond youth screamed above the din, "I'm going to cut the throat of that dirty Jew."

Friends at the academy kept assuring Einstein that all this was a gross but passing phase of the chaotic peace. They said it would help if he kept silent. Einstein laughed and said his view of Man was "too objective" for such things to disturb him.

However, former colleagues from Switzerland, visiting him for the first time since the war, found him noticeably embittered. One said he had "fallen into the cold prose of life." For the first time, Einstein was talking about "the rush of events" and he didn't mean scientific events. "The yellow press and other half-wits are at my heels to the point where I can scarcely draw breath, let alone do any really decent work," he complained.

In 1920 Einstein brought his mother from Switzerland to Berlin. She was nearing seventy and had been sick for some time. She died peacefully in his apartment the same year, proud of the world acclaim for her son's genius and happily ignorant of the forces so vindictively against him in Berlin. Einstein was saddened but not heart-broken. He mentioned to a friend soon afterwards that the thought of death in such dismal times was "almost cheering."

Einstein's voluntary involvement in the human drama had brought him nothing but trouble and had so shaken his fine detachment that he doubted he was any longer capable of scientific discovery. Yet he did not despair. In a message to American and British Quakers who had sent vast food shipments to Germany to feed starving children, Einstein praised their humanity and added that people must not abandon hope for a better world. His own rationality was preserved by his sense of humor as much as by anything else.

One night at the huge Berlin Philharmonic Hall, he bought a box seat for a "Relativity meeting" conducted by an anti-Semitic group of German scientists calling themselves the Working Committee of German Natural Philosophers. Two physicists, Weyland and Gehrcke, shared top billing and they raged for hours about the "Einstein hoax."

It was supposed to be a serious and angry evening, but it deteriorated into a farce because Einstein applauded wildly at the most innocuous moments and frequently threw back his head to release a raucous belly laugh. The audience was more entertained by the man in the box than the two men on the stage.

Late in the year, Einstein had a respite from the storm of hate. Lorentz and Ehrenfest called him back to Leyden to lecture the university body on Relativity. More than fourteen hundred people packed the hall and Einstein was given a standing ovation. Then Ehrenfest, who feared for his friend's safety in Berlin, urged him to stay at the university. He had persuaded the directors to offer Einstein a permanent position.

Life in Holland, with the chance of increased professional association with Lorentz who represented Einstein's idea of perfection both as a physicist and as a man, was most tempting. He took the problem back to Berlin and walked the streets. The center of the city, once the brightest spot in all Europe, was bleak and dark. There was no crush of traffic, no bright restaurants. Crowds wandered quietly and aimlessly in the phantom gloom. Posters on walls and doors pictured Bolshevism as a black gorilla with hands dripping blood. Here and there soldiers stood in doorways with machine guns crooked in their arms.

He thought over his problem carefully. A few months earlier, the Democrats had been re-elected to the Reichstag with a solid majority and the government had already received one vote of confidence. Nationalists were still powerful, but the Communists were fading. Coal production was slowly increasing and, although Germany's national debt ranged into hundreds of billions of marks, there was a wider hope now that it could be wiped out. If ever a true democracy was to evolve in Germany, this was the time.

Einstein decided he could not desert. He was a public figure. If he walked out now, people might get the idea he had been frightened away. This would be a bad reflection on the Republic. He must set an example, show his faith in the future of Germany. He would not only stay—he would take out German citizenship again. But because of his position at the academy, he could retain his Swiss citizenship as well.

In a letter to his family in Switzerland, Einstein was much less intense about his new feeling of responsibility. Hans Albert roared at his father's description of what it was like to be famous. And it reminded Mileva of the good days when Albert teased her by starting to tell risqué jokes . . .

"I feel now something like a whore," wrote Einstein. "Everybody wants to know what I am doing all the time and everybody wants to criticize."

CHAPTER 6

THE BARNUM OF PHYSICS

Leopold Infeld, a later associate of Einstein and then a physics student in Berlin, said 1920 was the start of "an era of hucksterism in popular science."

When Relativity first became famous, the only book in English giving a clear explanation of the theory was a thin volume called "Report on the Relativity Theory of Gravitation." It was written by Arthur Eddington in 1918 and had an initial sale of about two hundred copies. In 1920 the publishers turned out the book by the thousands. It was grabbed off the bookstalls in London and New York as if it were a racy novel.

The best-selling author agreed to lecture on Relativity to a university audience at Oxford. None of the halls was big enough to hold the crowd so the lecture was set for the cavernous student dining room. Eddington had to fight his way past a long queue of dons and students and tourists to get in. The room was already overflowing with people so he repeated his lecture for a "second house." It was such a hit that he published the lecture in book form under the title, *Space, Time and Gravitation*. And this also became a top seller.

Readers agreed most with the opening line of the final chapter in which Eddington discussed the more speculative aspects of Einstein's theory. The Englishman jokingly prefaced his remarks with a quotation from Hippolyte in *A Midsummer Night's Dream:* "This is the silliest stuff that ever I heard."

Silly or not, more than one hundred so-called laymen's books on Relativity reached the bookstores in 1920. Only one of them was Einstein's, an updated version of a comprehensive, less-mathematical account of his theory written by him in 1917. Einstein had read every page to Elsa's daughter Margot as he went along, asking whether she understood. Margot kept saying, "Yes, Albert." But the book was understood only by physicists, good physicists.

A philanthropic American, Eugene Higgins, who lived in Paris, troubled because he couldn't find a short and readable account of the theory, cabled the magazine *Scientific American* offering a five thousand dollar prize to the man who could best explain Relativity in three thousand words or less. The magazine launched the contest with appropriate fanfare and impecunious scientists from India to Iowa tried for the prize. After a long and frantic search, the editors found two American physicists who agreed to stay out of the contest. They were needed as judges.

The winner, among hundreds of entrants, was Lyndon Bolton. Ironically, Bolton was an examiner at the British Patent Office.

Relativity was given political and racial colors in Germany. People there were wary about Einstein. They thought he might be a fraud. But in other European countries he was in great demand. Einstein did not want to peddle his theory like a patent medicine, but the lecture requests gave him a chance to get away from the incessant snarling of his detractors. He packed a clean white collar, tucked a violin under his arm and headed off alone. He went to Norway and Holland first, then swung south to Prague and Vienna.

"When I met him at the station he had changed very little," recalled Philipp Frank, who had taken over Einstein's job in Prague ten years before. "He still looked like an itinerant violin virtuoso."

Frank accommodated his guest in his office at the university. Einstein wanted it that way. The world's newest scientific genius slept on a sofa and dined on calf's liver fried over a Bunsen burner. His lecture was such a success that he faced the rather incredible call of "encore, encore." Einstein announced that he had not yet worked out an encore to Relativity, so he played his violin instead.

Up to then, Einstein's audiences had consisted mostly of students and practicing scientists. But his university hosts in Vienna had hired a concert hall for him and opened a box office to sell tickets. The three thousand seats in the theater were sold out a week in advance and most of the buyers were regular concert goers who looked forward to a night of learning served with a touch of vaudeville. Einstein was reputed to be "a character."

Einstein, meanwhile, arrived at the station in Vienna in a third-class rail carriage. His host, the physicist Felix Ehrenhaft, and the reporters had trouble finding him. They had expected him to travel first class. When he saw him at the end of the train with his violin case, Ehrenhaft was touched by the simplicity of the man.

"You know, I like traveling first," he confided to the disappointed Ehrenhaft, "but my face is becoming too well known. I am less bothered in third class."

There was clamorous applause when Einstein walked on stage for his lecture. He looked disinterested.

"It is a mistake to force a public lecture on a dedicated scientist like Einstein," a local professor complained. "It's undignified. He must hate it."

"That's not what I heard in Zurich," said his companion. "He gave public lectures there. He sizes up his audience and tailors his material accordingly. In Zurich, they say he's a born actor. His friends say there's a lot of ham in Einstein."

Here in Vienna, Einstein started off dramatically. "I strike my hand twice against the table." His hand came down—one, two. "What is your description of these phenomena? You are inclined to say that two knocks, at different moments, have been delivered on the same spot. Is this true?"

Einstein paused and the people in the vast hall nodded.

"You are aware of course that this room placed as it is on earth is moving through space initially because the world is turning on its own axis and then because the world is revolving around the sun, and then because the solar system is itself moving through space. It was therefore wrong to say that two knocks were delivered at the same spot at two different times. The sameness of the spot was only relative to the room in which we were placed. And if we wanted the spot to remain the same in an absolute sense, we should have to annihilate the sense of time. That is, the two knocks must take place simultaneously.

"You see, therefore, that identity of place is only possible when the sense of time is absolutely annihilated, and that place is only relative to time. But the converse is equally true. That is to say, there is no time-sameness except when the factor of space ceases to exist.

"The simultaneity of two events is purely relative. For instance, suppose that at two points equidistant from you two flashes of light were to become simultaneously visible . . ."

The professor's soft voice was carrying right to the loges. There was not a sound in the house. The man was talking sense. It was all so obvious. Eagerly the people imagined two instant flashes of light at either side of the stage . . .

"You would be likely to say that since light travels with uniform speed and the two points were equidistant from you, the outbreaks of light occurred simultaneously. But were you and the two points of light stationary at the moment light reached your eyes? Of course not, for the earth itself is not stationary. And your motion with the earth necessarily affected the relativity to yourself of the speed of light. You were going toward one light and away from the other, and therefore one light came faster toward you and the other more slowly. Thus, what you saw simultaneously did not occur simultaneously . . ."

Einstein went on like this, one thought emphasized and re-emphasized at a time, until he had outlined the most vital concepts of Relativity. He chose his words carefully, avoiding generaly unfamiliar expressions like "inertial systems" and "classical thermodynamics."

Maurice Samuel, who covered the lecture for the *Manchester Guardian*, said people left the hall with the light of excitement in their eyes. "We became almost delirious with the joy of perfect understanding," he wrote.

Einstein could have made a small fortune lecturing on Relativity to the general public. But he knew when to draw the line. An English impresario cabled him saying he could guarantee a three-week booking at the London Paladium. Einstein treated the offer as a huge joke. He did not bother to reply.

When he returned to Berlin early in 1921, the Zionists asked him to tour the United States with Chaim Weizmann, the brilliant chemist who had assumed leadership of the Zionist movement. Weizmann wanted to raise money among the American Jews for the Palestine Foundation Fund. He wanted Einstein along because he thought the great physicist could awaken American interest in the Hebrew University. "The foundation stones for the university have been sitting alone on Mount Scopus for long enough," said Weizmann.

The idea of asking people for money did not appeal to Einstein. When Kurt Blumenfeld came for his answer, he said he would not go.

"If you take your Zionism seriously, you'll go," snapped Blumenfeld. "Weizmann is our leader. We must follow him."

"All right," said Einstein. "I'll go."

Later, he decided that he had jumped to the right decision. Zionist hopes might be fulfilled soon. The Balfour Declaration of 1917 pledged British support for establishing a Jewish national home in Palestine, and it was the British who controlled the Promised Land. Also, there was Weizmann's own high standing in England. During the war, he had been borrowed by the Admiralty from the University of Manchester and had much improved British high explosives. Weizmann said there were only one hundred thousand Jews in Palestine out of a world total of fifteen million. Droves of them wanted to settle in Zion but they lacked the means. Weizmann was out to get the means.

Einstein had a personal interest in the Hebrew University project. He had received scores of letters and visits from Jewish students in Russia, Poland and Romania, as well as Germany, who could not get into universities because of the growing anti-Semitism. Even with Max Planck's help, he himself was unable to end the discrimination at the University of Berlin. A Hebrew university could absorb some of these men. It could also serve to re-kindle Jewish idealism which had been dimmed, Einstein thought, by centuries of assimilation with western culture.

He was very conscious of his Judaism now. "The pursuit of knowledge for its own sake, an almost fanatical love of justice and the desire for personal independence—these are the features of the Jewish tradition which make me thank my lucky stars that I belong to it," he said.

The scientists at the Prussian Academy advised Einstein against the American trip. Fritz Haber, who had been listed as a war criminal but never put on trial, was adamant about it. Haber had converted from Judaism to Christianity. He said Einstein would seriously harm his career if he joined "the radical Weizmann." Einstein just smiled.

In the dawning spring of 1921, Albert and Elsa Einstein boarded the *Rotterdam* in Holland and sailed via Plymouth, where the Weizmanns embarked, to New York.

The curtain was then going up on the "Roaring Twenties," and the madness with which New York greeted Einstein and Weizmann was to become one of the early symbols of the era.

Radio was new and so was syncopated rhythm and the sweet cornet of Bix Beiderbecke. Fatty Arbuckle was playing in the movies and George M. Cohan was still the brightest light on Broadway. Greenwich Village was ecstatic about Carl Sandburg, but Ring Lardner wasn't bad, either. Babe Ruth was at bat and Jack Dempsey said he could lick that Frenchman Carpentier any time. Bootlegging was Jersey's new claim to fame. The cops winked at the Manhattan speakeasies, but they uncovered a divorce mill in Westchester. Rockefeller was giving away a large part of his money. Jewel thieves were having a picnic on New York's East Side. Everywhere, "Look For The Silver Lining" was being played in double time.

Sailing serenely into the din on that cool Saturday of April 2 came the *Rotterdam,* with Einstein on deck watching six fast harbor boats racing toward him from the Battery. Behind, on the quays, there was pandemonium—jostling people, jamming cars, sweating mounted police. Horns were blaring and a thousand flags waved above the mob. Einstein wondered what all the fuss was about.

The pack of reporters and photographers ran down Albert and Elsa Einstein on the boat deck. Cornered with no escape, Einstein looked stricken as cameramen fired at him from all angles and men with notebooks shouted questions in his ear. This must be an American phenomenon, he thought.

The wonder went both ways. The name "Einstein" had become part of the New York lingo. It signified anything that was incomprehensible—as in "it's all Einstein to me"—and it was used as the ultimate refuge of a person who was posed a difficult problem—as in "who d'yuh think I am, Einstein?" It was a shock to see the name suddenly materialized in flesh and bone. The name had conjured up a vague man-like figure with a big bald head with equations written all over it. Yet here was the genuine article—a man in a faded gray overcoat and a floppy black felt hat that couldn't quite conceal the gray hair straggling over his ears. He gave the impression of an immigrant shoemaker who had been hounded out of the Ukraine. The way he clutched a new briar pipe in his hand made it seem his most treasured possession.

When Einstein only continued to look bewildered and kept muttering in German, the reporters hurried him bodily along the deck into the captain's cabin to find an interpreter. Mayor John Hylan was waiting there, with the official hand of the city extended and a silent prayer on his lips that none of the reporters would call his famous guest "Al."

Einstein weathered the usual questions about the skyline, Prohibition and American women, then faced the inevitable request to explain Relativity in one sentence.

"I have been trying for years to condense the theory into one book and have not succeeded," he said graciously. The city desk would not be satisfied with this. The question was repeated. "It is a theory of space and time," offered Einstein hopefully.

"Ah, c'mon, Professor, we need a little more than that."

"Well, just as a joke and not to be taken too literally, Relativity has this effect on any thought of the universe: up to this time the conceptions of time and space have been such that if everything in the universe were taken away, if there was nothing left, then there would still remain to Man time and space. But under my theory, even time and space would cease to exist because they are inseparably bound up with the conceptions of matter."

That was good . . . "Einstein said today he had destroyed time and space."

The rest of the interview resulted in the information that Einstein was puzzled to account for public interest in Relativity. "It seems psycho-pathological," he said with a laugh. He shrugged noncommittally at a suggestion that people were intrigued because the universe was next to the idea of God.

Weizmann, who had gracefully accepted the fact that Zionism was taking second place to Einsteinism, suspected that his friend's geniality was wearing thin. He spirited him away to an empty cabin to wait for nightfall. The ship had berthed, but it was the Jewish Sabbath and the Zionist group could not go ashore until after sunset.

The mayor's boat took them across the river from the Hoboken dock to Manhattan, where they were escorted through a crowding throng of cheering citizens. Einstein held tightly to his hat and his pipe as people lunged for souvenirs. The Einsteins and the Weizmanns were loaded into a long black car, which then crawled off through the streets of lower Manhattan at the head of a mile-long noisy motorcade. Second Avenue was lined on both sides with what seemed to be all of New York's Jewry. Zionist flags of white and blue were gripped in raised fists and people crushed forward to grab the eager hand of Professor Weizmann and to gape at the modern Spinoza by his side. Deafened by the bedlam outside, startled at the blizzard of confetti and fearful that he might be dragged out of the car, Einstein hunched down into his coat.

It was past midnight when the travelers finally crawled into their beds at the Commodore Hotel in mid-town. The hardy Weizmann confessed that the day had left him tired, hungry, thirsty and dazed. Einstein, the main victim of the mob onslaught, had been so severely jolted that he was in a near state of shock.

A new horror awaited him in the morning when he saw the Sunday newspapers that had been delivered to his room. Einstein did not speak much English, but he could read it. His name and flippant shipboard comments blared at him from every front page. The stories were friendly—some called him a "sweet, kindly man"—but, to the hero himself, they were the press notices of a circus freak rather than a man of science. Einstein, one paper reminded its readers, had proved that

102

space was curved and therefore that a man using a powerful enough telescope would see the back of his own head.

Hours later, a distraught Elsa Einstein reported a missing husband. She had left him alone in their room reading the newspapers but when she returned he was gone. She had searched about the hotel and looked in the street outside, but no Albert. The mystery was cleared up when a bellhop checked the roof and found a man sitting propped against a ventilator funnel, dreamily playing a violin.

Einstein never really got accustomed to the uproar of New York, but his first violent reaction passed as the days went by and the realization came that the town wasn't vulgar—just high-spirited. In fact, the carnival air was quite invigorating after the wretchedness of Berlin. The people of the city radiated self-confidence and they seemed totally devoid of envy, despite the extremes of personal wealth. Einstein was staggered to find that a private corporation owned the railroad to Boston, and that traditionally—for Europe—state-owned services like the telegraph and telephone were in private hands. Yet nowhere did he see the arrogance he associated with wealth and position. There was no obvious class distinction, nobody he could call downtrodden. Wages were high and so was the standard of living. The girl who did the typing at the hotel was as finely dressed as any high-born woman he had seen in Berlin. The New World worked, he decided, because the people had a "social conscience."

As a genuine, just imported, not-to-be-missed celebrity, Einstein was denied the privacy and dignity that were a part of the democratic life. He was the target of stares wherever he went; he once said he felt in a constant state of undress. The best he could look forward to at the endless round of cocktail and tea parties, Zionist rallies and stuffy dinners was the few minutes he could properly hide himself in a washroom.

He tried, uselessly, to belittle his theories in the public eye. "The contrast between the popular estimate of my powers and achievements and the reality is simply grotesque," he insisted.

America's most eminent scientists honored him with hair-raising eulogies at a special meeting of the National Academy of Sciences in Washington. He protested, almost in the manner of a teacher trying to calm over-exuberant students. "When a man, after long years of searching, chances upon a thought that discloses something of the beauty of this mysterious universe, he should not be personally celebrated," he said. "He is already sufficiently paid by his experience of seeking and finding. In science, moreover, the work of the individual is so bound up with that of his scientific predecessors and contemporaries that it seems almost an impersonal product of his generation."

Einstein most enjoyed the three days he spent at Princeton University in New Jersey. It was a serene and stately institution that could have been transplanted from southern Germany. "A fine place," said Einstein, "like a pipe as yet unsmoked." He gave three lectures on Relativity there, all aimed at a graduate audience. He looked askance at the reporters scribbling in the front row. A few days later, the professor who had translated Einstein's talks from German into English told Einstein that Carr Vattel Van Anda, the managing editor of *The New York Times,* thought he had found an error in Einstein's first lecture. One of the equations did not make sense.

The way Meyer Berger recalled the incident in his book, *The Story of the New York Times*, Einstein "scanned his notes and nodded. He said, 'Yes, Mr. Van Anda is right. I made a mistake in transcribing the equation on the blackboard.'" From this time on, Einstein had a special respect for the *New York Times*.

Einstein and Weizmann spent most of their time in the United States traveling and making speeches—or rather—Weizmann made the speeches. After the first few towns on a campaign route that looped from New York to Boston via the mid-west, Einstein restricted his public addresses to two sentences: "Weizmann is your one leader. Follow him." It was an impassioned call because Einstein was amazed and delighted at his bearded friend's statesmanship. There was a greatness about Weizmann that made him the Ezra of the second restoration in the eyes of many Zionists. Einstein could not hope to share this particular pedestal and, in any case, he knew that his most vital role in the repugnant business of asking for money was as a drawing card.

The traveling routine was man-killing. They arrived in towns by early trains and were paraded through the streets by a horde of enthusiasts. Breakfast at the city hall was followed by a round of speeches, and then came the press conference. Einstein was always asked to define Relativity and Weizmann was always asked how he hit on the invention of TNT. Weizmann had nothing to do with the invention of TNT, but his denials were interpreted as modesty. The two men were given a half hour for a bath before lunch, which meant more speeches, and soon it was time for the afternoon session with prominent local Jews. The day concluded with a mass meeting at the city hall. Then, it was back to the train and on to the next town where the whole process was repeated.

"This went on for weeks," said Weizmann later.

Much to Einstein's dismay, there was little excitement about the Hebrew University. It sounded too ambitious to the American Jews. At some places, Einstein had the authority to collect checks for the university, but several would-be donors admitted that they were wary about entrusting Einstein with the money. This was no reflection on his honesty. It was just that he did not seem businesslike, a practical man of affairs. None would have been surprised to know that Einstein had once used a check from a publishing house as a bookmark and probably would have still been using it if Elsa Einstein had not idly thumbed through the book one day.

But money for the Palestine Foundation Fund poured in. By the end of the year, Weizmann had raised more than two million dollars, enough to go ahead with land purchase and settlement. This success was due to Einstein's peculiar power as a human magnet and to Weizmann's gift for dramatizing the cause of Zionism.

"When a pioneer comes to Palestine, he finds a deserted land, neglected for generations," Weizmann told the Jews gathered in halls across the country. "The hills have lost their trees, the good soil has been washed into the valleys and carried to the sea. We must restore the soil of Palestine. We must have money to sink in Palestine, to reconstruct what has been destroyed. You will have to sweat and labor and give money on which you will not get any return but which will be transformed into national wealth. When you drain the marshes, you get no returns, but you accumulate wealth for the generations to come. If you reduce the percentage of malaria from forty to ten, that is national wealth . . . Give us your help. I am trying to build up a country which has been waste for two thousand years."

Einstein, like most other Jews, was deeply stirred by Weizmann's evangelism, but his obsession with physics remained unshaken throughout the tour. He sneaked off to the physics laboratories of universities whenever he could to talk with students and debate with their professors. He was surprised at the intensity of advanced research here, for Europe considered the United States a second-class scientific country. Relativity was the big excitement down the corridors Einstein liked to wander and it was refreshing for him even to hear his theory attacked, for here there was no political motive.

He got the full range of American opinion at New York's Columbia University where Charles Lane Poor, the professor of celestial mechanics, and Michael Pupin, the professor of electromechanics, had locked horns over Relativity. Both men ranked as giants in the American academic world.

When he went to Columbia, Einstein was introduced by Pupin as the man who had "lifted the veil to reality with a theory that could not have been created except by a mind which has the subtle qualities of the Hebrew prophets."

"Bah," said Poor. "The Einstein theory with its conflicting formulae and inaccuracies has caused more sins to be committed in the name of Relativity than can be attributed to any other modern scientific postulate."

Einstein had a little more patience with Poor who at least backed his denunciation with constructive thoughts, than he did with other American detractors who called him the "P. T. Barnum of physics." But he could not understand why any man of learning should not see the essential truth in his theory —and he said so.

Later, after his return to Berlin, a Dutch newspaper quoted him as saying that "it made a ridiculous impression on me to observe the excitement of Americans over a theory of which they understood nothing."

New Yorkers interpreted this as sour grapes, but Einstein, denying that he had said any such thing, hurried off a statement to soothe ruffled feelings: "It is a gratifying sign of our age—so often criticized for being materialistic—that it makes heroes of men whose goals rest upon purely spiritual and moral bases. According to my experience, this idealistic attitude prevails in America in an especially high degree . . ."

The quote in the Dutch newspaper was probably closer to Einstein's true feelings about his American reception. Often he told friends that he could not pretend to be flattered by his acclamation in New York when he realized that a prizefighter got the same treatment. And it must not have escaped his notice that at the Commodore Hotel where he spent hours hiding from reporters and autograph hunters, a young actor from Hollywood had exactly the same trouble. The two comprised the oddest team in the history of the New York celebrity system—Einstein and Jackie Coogan, aged five.

On the way back to Germany, Einstein visited London. Most Englishmen still detested anything and anyone from Germany. Einstein knew this. But he decided to risk the visit because Lord Haldane, the statesman and philosopher, wrote him that his doing so would open the door to resumption of pre-war scientific exchange between the two countries.

Immediately after they landed at Liverpool, the Einsteins were driven to Haldane's country mansion near London. They were unnerved the moment they stepped through the door. Elegance sniffed at them. It was the most non-sauerkraut place Elsa had ever seen in her life. She recounted the details later to friends:

After a late dinner of grilled spatchcock, they were put in the charge of a tall, funereal butler. Keeping them at arm's length, he marched them up stairs and along ringing corridors to a mammoth bedroom. Wordlessly, he pulled the drapes, turned down the covers on the huge Tudor bed and backed out the door. Albert and Elsa undressed tidily, blew out the candles with deliberate puffs and quietly sank into the bed. They whispered their goodnights. In the morning, Albert opened his eyes and peered about for the butler. He thought he might be waiting to dress him.

"Shall I ring for a cup of tea?" Elsa asked. Her voice smashed about the room. Albert looked stricken.

"Sh . . sh . . That man might come back. Lie still. Perhaps they will forget us." Albert pulled the covers up to his chin, prepared to stay in the bed for the rest of his life. It was another hour before Elsa got him moving.

Scientists who attended Einstein's lecture on Relativity in the great hall of King's College in London said they could feel a tremor in the air when he walked on stage with Haldane. Every seat was taken. Scotland Yard men were spotted among the students who stood against the walls. Down in the front row, Dr. Abraham Shalom Yahuda, the Orientalist, heard two men whispering.

"Do you think anything will happen?" said one.

"I don't know," said the other. "Einstein is lecturing in German. That won't go down too well."

"Look at all those young fellows," said the first man. "Surely they didn't come to listen to a talk in German on an abstruse thing like Relativity."

Yahuda leaned over and interrupted the whisperers. "Calm down, gentlemen. Einstein is the greatest scientist in the world. That's why we are all here. Nothing will happen."

There was no applause when Einstein walked in and still no applause when Haldane introduced him as "the Newton of the Twentieth Century." Einstein came dreamily to the rostrum and started his lecture. He talked into the silence for more than an hour, then moved back to his chair. Somebody started clapping. A few others joined in. Suddenly, the whole audience was applauding. Rows of men in the front stood up and clapped with their hands held high in front of them so that everybody could see. The ovation kept up for three minutes, an acclaim for genius and an acclaim for courage. Only the reporter for the *Nation* did not join the applause. He scribbled excitedly: "This is the turning point . . . sanity, understanding and harmony are being restored by men of creative genius . . ."

Einstein went home happy. In Berlin he personally assured President Ebert that "better times are coming."

However, he decided that he had earned some time to himself. More than eighteen months as a leading member of the human race had been heart-rewarding to a certain extent. But only science could please his soul. He had set himself a new aim: find the mathematical connection between the two great universal fields—electromagnetism and gravitation. This would be a first step in discovering the laws governing the conduct of everything in the universe, from the smallest electron to the largest planet. Einstein felt intuitively that there was such a connection. This was enough for him. He remembered telling the professors in Princeton that everything must work according to a well laid-out plan, that nothing was "chancy" about the universe: *Raffiniert ist der Herrgott, aber boshaft ist er nicht"*—"God is clever, but he is not malicious." He did not know that his words had even then been carved into a mantelpiece at Princeton.

Through the fall and winter months, Einstein worked in his attic, with only a short break to fulfill his annual lecturing contract with the University of Leyden. He refused to see reporters and he warned Elsa not to accept any social engagements for him. Romain Rolland's sister Madeleine wrote from Paris, asking him to sponsor a youth peace rally in Italy. He declined. His friend Paul Langevin repeatedly asked him to lecture on Relativity at the College de France in Paris. He kept saying no.

Night after night he paced the floor of his attic. He smoked heavily. He ate little. His brain searched one blind alley after another. Nothing.

Walther Rathenau snapped him out of it in the spring of 1922. The two were good friends. Rathenau told Einstein about politics and Einstein told Rathenau about theoretical physics. Rathenau was the most outspoken Democrat in all Germany. He was a wealthy Jew who had eagerly accepted the role of German Foreign Minister. His policy was to pay the war reparations, build the Republic and restore the greatness of Germany. His immediate problem was to convert the energy being spent in hating France to more constructive purposes. Einstein had helped patch relations between English and German scholars. Now he must do his bit to improve Franco-German relations.

Einstein admitted to Rathenau that his refusals to lecture at the College de France had troubled his conscience. He would take a rest from his scientific research and go to Paris.

Langevin and Maurice Solovine, Einstein's old school friend, boarded the Paris express at the Belgian border to warn Einstein of possible demonstrations against him in Paris. After some trouble, they found him in his customary third-class coach seat. As a precaution, they escorted him off the back of the train when it pulled into Paris and hustled him through an alley to a waiting car.

It sped off into the night with Einstein's rollicking laughter drowning out the roar of the exhaust.

His apprehensions vanished with the first whiff of Paris in the spring. *Joie de vivre* was perking through the mush of resentment and hate. He thought even Haldane's butler might like it here. One or two of the newspapers said Einstein was not welcome and several physicists announced that they would not attend his lecture. But this petulance was balanced by a beaming editorial in a liberal newspaper: "Einstein in Paris! It is the victory of the archangel over the demon of the abyss." His lecture was well received and his private talks afterwards with Madame Curie, the philosopher Henri Bergson and others increased his optimism. They all agreed that the time for revenge was over. The intellectuals must ease the bitterness between France and Germany.

Solovine reminded him later that hard-headed politicians were running the world, not idealistic scholars. This was a truth that Einstein had known only too clearly during the war. Now, however, he wanted to believe that men of goodwill could exert telling influence.

"*You* can because of your great renown," Solovine told him. Like others before him, Solovine wanted to keep Einstein in the human struggle. On an impulse he drove him to the northern French city of Saint-Quentin. The war had dynamited Saint-Quentin almost out of existence. Einstein walked through the ruins, his face white and troubled. "This is terrible, terrible," he muttered. "There must be no more war. It must be abolished . . . at all costs."

His hopes soared two months later when a large group of French and German pacifists gathered in the Reichstag for a friendship rally. Early in the meeting, a Frenchman jumped to his feet and pointed to Einstein in the audience. "There is living proof that the scholars of France and Germany can work together as brothers," he shouted. Einstein ducked his head as the crowd turned to him and cheered wildly.

113

Two weeks later Walther Rathenau was murdered in the street by right-wing thugs.

Einstein was shattered. Rathenau was a good man. Rathenau was the main pillar of the Republic. The faculty heads of the University of Berlin suggested a memorial service and asked Einstein to participate. Angrily he said a service was not enough. The University should stage a public meeting to protest political gangsterism. There was no reaction.

Colleagues at the Prussian Academy heard that Einstein was marked for assassination. They made him stay away from the office and the university. They told the newspapers that Einstein had left the country for a holiday.

But reporters can be smarter than professors. They found Einstein and wanted to know why he had canceled his lectures. He refused to admit that he was supposed to be in hiding.

"I'm tired of being looked at like a chorus girl in an animal cage," he joked. "At my last lecture, girl students were peering at me through opera glasses. I've also found that I get my highest attendances on rainy nights when other sight-seeing is impossible."

Elsa Einstein was worried sick over Albert's plight. Almost forcibly she kept him in the house for two weeks. Then he decided to have no more of it. *If they really want to kill me, I'll give them their chance.* It was August 1 and a horde of students, housewives and liberal-minded men from all walks of life was assembling at the outskirts of the city for an auto parade. Their banners read: NO MORE WAR. Einstein went to the head of the column and took his place in the back seat of an open car. Everybody in Berlin knew his face. It had been on the covers of a dozen magazines. It had appeared numerous times in newspaper pictures. Berliners saw it again that day, defiant and unsmiling, as Einstein was paraded through the streets.

The next day he left for a long visit to the University of Leyden. He traveled, as usual, by train. A heavy-set man in the seat opposite watched him all the way. Once, when a man came lurching down the aisle and nearly stumbled into Einstein's lap, the heavy-set man bolted half out of his seat. The pedestrian kept going and the man relaxed. Einstein was oblivious to the incident; he never noticed his bodyguard— secretly hired by Elsa Einstein.

Even after Leyden, Einstein could not settle back into his work. He wanted to get away from Berlin. This was no problem. By late 1922, Relativity was known and discussed all over the world and Einstein had had invitations to many countries, all expenses paid. Early in October, Albert and Elsa took a train to Marseilles and boarded a Japanese steamer for a six-month tour of the Orient.

CHAPTER 7

"GOD DOESN'T PLAY DICE"

Einstein stepped off the gangplank in Colombo, Ceylon, and came face to face with a tall, brown Hindu in a soiled loin cloth. He looked bald all over. Muscle and sinew seemed ready to burst through his thin and dusty skin. His face was fine-boned and his eyes proud. Brown saliva trickled from a corner of his mouth. To Einstein, the man looked like a squalid nobleman. This description was the best he could think of on the spur of the moment.

The Hindu grabbed Einstein's arm and said something that sounded like *"j'nrickshah-sarb."* He hauled Einstein away and sat him on a lean pillow in a one-man rickshaw. Then he stepped between the long shafts and started to trot away.

"No, no," bellowed Einstein. "For God's sake, put me down." The native stopped, bewildered. Einstein lunged off his perch. He looked around and saw Elsa being escorted to another rickshaw. "Stop," he yelled.

A ship's officer arrived on the scene and Einstein peered

at him as if it were all his fault. "This is barbaric," he accused.

The officer agreed. But he reminded Einstein that he was now in the East. This meant a change of custom as well as scenery. He advised Einstein to take the rickshaw.

"All around. Two rupee. Two rupee," the Hindu pleaded, his fists bunched under his chin and his arms pressed to his chest. Einstein thought the native was about to squat and hug him about the knees. Hastily he got back into the rickshaw and told Elsa to do so, too. Off they went with their human ponies grinning in front.

"I was bitterly ashamed," Einstein recorded in his diary that night. "But I couldn't do anything about it. These beggars of regal stature hurl themselves at every tourist until he capitulates. They know how to beg and implore in a way which tears your heart. Along the streets of the native quarter, one sees how these attractive people live their primitive lives. For all their nobility, they give one the impression that the climate prevents them from thinking back or ahead more than a quarter hour. They live at ground level, amid great filth and a considerable stench, do little and need little. Their quarters are much too crowded to allow the individual any privacy. Half-naked, they exhibit beautiful and muscular bodies, with fine, patient features. There is no such hubbub as among the Levantines in Port Said, no brutality, no turbulence—only a quiet submissiveness, not without a certain serenity. Looking at these people closely, one loses one's appetite for Europeans who are so much more degenerate and brutal, look so much coarser and greedier. This, unfortunately, accounts for their superiority in practical affairs, their capacity to conceive big things and carry them through. I wonder whether we would be like the Hindus in this climate . . . There is much activity in the harbor. Herculean workers with glossy black bodies load and unload the cargo. Divers engage in their daring performances. And always a smile on their faces when they sacrifice themselves for filthy money and for sated people who are mean enough to enjoy all that . . ."

Einstein sailed on to Singapore, Hong Kong, Shanghai. He felt like Marco Polo. For a while at least, the universe was forgotten. Now, for the first time, he was discovering the earth. "Let us take it all in before we wake up," he told his wife as their ship ploughed past the sampans and junks to an open dock at Shanghai. Children from the German school there were singing a German song. Chinese and European officials and scholars waited to welcome him. But his eyes went to the coolies toting huge bales and boxes on thin shoulders. Further back he saw a huddle of Chinese men and women repairing a cobbled road. They were cracking large gray stones with mallets and then banging the chips into the rough road surface. A blowsy European overseer stood off to one side.

"The way the Europeans lord it over the Chinese is disgusting," he wrote later. "They abuse them worse than cattle."

Einstein found a five-day-old cable waiting for him in Shanghai. It was from the Swedish Academy of Science. He had been awarded the Nobel Prize for physics "for your photoelectric law and your work in the field of theoretical physics." His photoelectric law, advancing Planck's quantum theory of matter, was seventeen years old. There was no mention of Relativity, his real triumph. The Nobel committee was playing safe. Relativity was still too controversial. But the committee could not ignore Einstein indefinitely. He *was* the most famous physicist since Newton. Thus, a compromise that made Einstein laugh.

Japan so delighted Einstein that he stayed there more than two months He traveled up and down the breath-taking country, lecturing and laughing. The people were naive, wonderfully naive. "The attitude of the Japanese towards authority is respectful, without a trace of cynicism or even skepticism," he wrote. "They have pure souls that can be found nowhere else among men. I love and respect this land."

He heard that shortly before he arrived in Tokyo the Diet had discussed an official message of welcome. The meeting collapsed into a wild argument about Relativity. It developed that nobody had the faintest notion of what it was all about, although one member said he had read Einstein's book from cover to cover. He quoted its title as *The Relation of Man to Woman*. Nevertheless, Einstein did get his official welcome, an audience with Emperor Yoshihito and four hours of deep silence while he explained his theories at Keio-Gijuka University. An interpreter did his best to make Einstein clear.

Einstein wanted to cut the time of subsequent lectures, but it was carefully pointed out to him that this would be regarded as a slight by the new audiences. If he gave four hours in Tokyo, he must give four hours in Kobe. The fact that few, if any, understood him was immaterial.

Gifts were pressed on the Einsteins at every town and they found it impossible to refuse them. In any case, Albert liked presents if they were not too elaborate. In addition to the silks and paintings and china, Einstein most prized a new violin and a bound book of drawings by Japanese schoolchildren. In Japan, even signing his autograph was a pleasure. Instead of a stubby pencil and a scrap of paper, he was handed a long brush dipped in violet ink and a piece of silk. He painted his name.

Einstein said he shed a few tears when he left Japan. This was part emotion, and partly because he had sensitive tear ducts. Even a slight breeze would set him weeping. His father and his sons had the same weakness. But he really loved Japan and it pained him to write, a little later: "Japan is like a great kettle without a safety valve. She has not enough land to enable her population to exist and develop. The situation must somehow be remedied if we are to avoid a terrible conflict."

Zionist leaders insisted that Einstein visit Palestine on the return voyage to Europe. He obliged readily. He wanted to see the reconstruction work. But first, he had to survive the tumult. He was feted extravagantly as "the most outstanding Jew in the world," a title bestowed on him in a readers' poll conducted by the American *Jewish Tribune*.

When he did travel through the country, he was staggered. He wrote his impressions in one long, breathless sentence: "When one sees young pioneers, men and women of magnificent intellectual and moral caliber, breaking stones and building roads under the blazing rays of the Palestinian sun; when one sees flourishing agricultural settlements shooting up from the long-deserted soil under the intensive efforts of the Jewish settlers; when one sees the development of water power and the beginnings of an industry adapted to the needs and possibilities of the country, and, above all, the growth of an educational system ranging from the kindergarten to the university, in the language of the Bible—what observer, whatever his origin or faith, can fail to be seized by the magic of such amazing achievements and of such superhuman devotion?"

His sabbatical over, Einstein returned to Berlin in the spring of 1923, anxious to resume his work. He was forever uncertain of just how much was expected of him in the field of human affairs. He felt he had done enough for a while. He was also disheartened because some of the projects he had joined were not developing properly.

His first action was to resign from the Committee on Intellectual Co-operation, set up within the League of Nations. He had joined the Committee the year before, but had not attended any meetings. When the French and Belgians occupied the Ruhr in January because Germany was not making good on coal reparations, Einstein considered that act a violation of the whole spirit of the League of Nations. League members had committed aggression with impunity. He would not be party to this travesty. He wanted the League to become a powerful supranational organization, with strict laws aimed at one prime objective: the abolition of war. When it lived up to this promise he would support the League again.

By his resignation, Einstein risked losing valued friends. One of them was Madame Curie. He had helped persuade her to join the committee when it was founded. Madame Curie was what Einstein called "the true Jacob," the really pure scientist. She had resisted interruptions to her work all her life.

This time, however, she had agreed to offer a piece of herself to the fight for internationalism. Now Einstein had left her in the lurch. He wrote her a letter of explanation, but she did not reply.

Einstein also summarily rejected an invitation to the Solvay scientific congress in Brussels. Lorentz and Ehrenfest both urged him to come, but that made no difference. Other Berlin scientists had not been invited and this, to Einstein, was a poor example for intellectuals to set for the world.

That summer he went to Göteborg, Sweden, to deliver his speech of acceptance for the Nobel Prize. Dozens of the world's most celebrated scientists gathered in full dress. The King of Sweden made his entrance, upright and elegant. Einstein was off stage at the moment, dressed in an old dinner jacket and a bulky black tie.

"We can easily send out for ah . . er . . more formal suit if you prefer," someone suggested.

Einstein flicked the sleeves of his jacket with his fingertips. "It's all right," he said. "We can put a sign on my back: 'This suit has just been brushed.' "

Then he went in to make his address. He was expected to speak on his photoelectric discovery, named specifically in the prize preamble. He did not even mention it. Instead, he talked about Relativity. Later, he stuffed the prize check, worth forty-five thousand dollars, into his pocket, and went home.

It was more money than Einstein had ever had in his life and he did not want it wasted. Elsa had made a few poor investments. Unlike Mileva, she sometimes speculated for quick profits. He decided that Mileva would put the money to the best use, so he sent her all of it. Half its value was lost in the exchange, but Mileva appreciated the gesture. She knew that the Ruhr occupation and the German Government's calculated inflation of the mark had made Germany bankrupt. Einstein's salary from the Prussian Academy was almost worthless now. One million paper marks were worth only one American dollar.

Although he had two families to support—and he had always been generous with Mileva—Einstein managed to keep solvent, even though he refused to make money out of his pure science and had accepted only traveling expenses on lecture trips. His main source of extra income was two or three large German industrial companies who retained him as a consultant. As a patent expert, he frequently prepared claims for these companies. He also appeared in court for them in infringement cases. Einstein followed technical science closely and sometimes his advice was invaluable. He urged one company to mass-produce gas refrigerators, and it made a fortune. Another firm wanted to test instruments in an airplane. Einstein gleefully went for a joy ride and made his report.

Zurich was only ten hours from Berlin by train, and Einstein went there often to seek Mileva's advice on investments. He enjoyed his first family. Hans Albert was well into his engineering course; his father now decided that the boy had made the right choice after all. Fourteen-year-old Teddy was brilliant. He had his father's passion for learning. But, unlike his father, whose memory was faulty, he could remember every single thing he had read or heard. Albert admired the lad tremendously. Yet he had a strange sense of foreboding. He felt it strongly when his son was playing the piano. His technique was perfect, but his playing had no personality. When a piece needed special interpretation and feeling, Teddy simply played the notes. It sounded wooden. Einstein explained how the music should be played. But his son could never do it.

During these brief interludes, Mileva and the boys were keenly aware of Albert's love for them. It was heart-felt love. "While it was there, it was very strong," remembered the older boy. "He needed to be loved himself. But almost the instant you felt the contact, he would push you away. He would not let himself go. He would turn off his emotion like a tap."

For the sake of his work, Einstein did not stay too long in Zurich. Mileva wondered if Berlin was any better for him. He was too much in the public eye. She was proud of his fame, however. Secretly, she wished it were herself—not Elsa—who was sharing it. She had been with him in Berne, helping him when he toiled so hard over Relativity by the kerosene lamp. Still, even now, she could follow his career and worry about him without bitterness. In the fall of 1923 she worried about him again because German nationalist reactionaries used the depression as another excuse to stir up trouble against liberals and Jews.

In Berlin, obscene and threatening letters reappeared in Einstein's mail and Elsa urged him to get out of town. Obediently, he went off to Leyden late in October. When the Prussian Academy announced his absence, right-wing newspapers suggested that Einstein might have defected to Russia. Even the more liberal newspapers, equating radical pacifism with strong leftist views, were becoming testy about Einstein. One of them published a cabled dispatch saying that Einstein had arrived in St. Petersburg.

Meanwhile, in Leyden, Einstein and Ehrenfest were discussing the problems of uniting gravitation and electricity. Einstein saw no newspapers until the middle of November. Then he read a story from Munich about a skinny young firebrand named Adolf Hitler. He had assembled a small army under the symbol of a twisted cross. Hitler had tried to take over Bavaria by cornering its leaders at gunpoint in a beer hall. Later he marched on Munich. The coup had failed and Hitler was arrested for treason. Einstein wondered if this dangerous young man had attended the Luitpold Gymnasium. He threw the paper away. "As I was saying, Ehrenfest, the weakness of that equation . . ."

Although Einstein attracted more publicity than Henry Ford or a Hollywood motion picture star, he appeared in the news only intermittently at this time.

In June, 1924, it was announced from the League of Nations headquarters in Geneva that Einstein had re-joined the Committee on Intellectual Co-operation. By this time, the Allies had greatly reduced reparations demands and had agreed to make generous loans so that Germany could rebuild. The League was working on machinery to outlaw war. The admission of Germany to the League was freely speculated. In Berlin, Einstein made a public statement, praising what seemed to be an all-European resolve to "let bygones be bygones." A later report said he had attended his first committee meeting and had been seen having breakfast in Geneva with Madame Curie.

The following year, Einstein turned up in South America. Crowds lined the streets in Buenos Aires, Montevideo and other cities and threw flowers at him. Spanish books on Relativity adorned shop windows. One Argentine newspaper charged that Einstein was anti-Catholic and Einstein commented "that reminds me of home," and that was all there was to it.

One other thing about the trip was noteworthy. Despite Einstein's sour reputation among politicians at home, in South America he was rosily greeted by German ambassadors and businessmen. "Strange people, these Germans," Einstein wrote in his diary. "I am a foul-smelling flower to them, yet they keep tucking me into their buttonholes."

During this period of reasonable calm in human events, physics was moving swiftly ahead. Einstein was fully involved. As he told a friend: "Politics are for the moment. An equation is for eternity."

The big story was the so-called quantum theory of nature. Physicists had found that things like trees and stones were made of atoms. An atom consisted of a positively charged nucleus surrounded by orbiting negatively charged electrons—a miniature solar system. It seemed reasonable to assume that an electron was the tiniest building block used by nature to construct the material things in the universe. It was impossible to to see, but was generally visualized as a hard little sphere.

Then, in the early Twenties, Einstein's thinking started to nudge the atomic physicists into a more definitive examination of the electron. They were dealing with matter, but Einstein had found matter was closely related to energy. He said that light traveled helter-skelter in separate little "photons" or light quanta. This particle theory of light had been proved by experiment, but so had the older wave theory. Physicists, including Einstein, agreed that light must be both corpuscular and wave-like. They could not draw a picture of it, but that did not really matter. There was a limit to Man's senses.

In 1924, a dashing young French physicist named Louis de Broglie decided that what was good for light was good for electrons. They, too, had wave and corpuscular personalities. Einstein was delighted. De Broglie thought "big." The wave characteristics were then proved by experiment. They were given mathematical interpretation.

The old question was brought up again. Exactly what *was* an electron? Was it really like a golf ball, an excited worm or a skein of wool? Nobody knew. Apparently it had a split personality. Accurate equations were worked out to forecast the actions of a whole bunch of electrons. Yet the behavior of a single electron under various circumstances could not be determined. It was a will-o'-the-wisp. Intensive inquiry showed that even if a scientist found an electron's position, he could not pin-point the velocity. If he found the velocity, he could not determine the position. A man needed light by which to see, and the photons or waves in this light played havoc with an electron. Scientists had reached a dead end. They acknowledged this by saying that nature, after all, had an inherent law of probability. All happenings in the universe were not predetermined by strict laws. In effect, an electron had a free will. There was an element of chance in what it might do next.

Einstein did not refute the worth of the quantum theory. He

had contributed largely to it himself. But he saw the theory merely as a suitable stopgap until something better and more definitive came long. Newton's theory of gravitation had been proved "correct" until Einstein gave it a different cast which seemed to interpret gravitation the way it really was. The probability factor in the quantum theory went against his grain. He did not believe in free will. He was a cause-and-effect man.

"God," he said, "doesn't play dice with the universe." The electron was not like the silver ball in a spinning roulette wheel. It abided by laws, just as did everything else in nature.

And so it was in the late Twenties that Einstein parted company with most theoretical physicists. They felt future physics must proceed on the premise of the quantum theory. Einstein doggedly persevered with his unified field theory, trying to express the actions of planets and electrons alike in one set of equations. Scientists did not argue about the idea of a unified theory. Many were seeking it. But Einstein's particular approach—to build on general Relativity without taking into account the quantum theory—was considered hopeless.

"Many of us regard this as a tragedy, both for him, as he gropes his way in loneliness, and for us, who miss our leader and standard-bearer," said Max Born.

Scientists did not lose their veneration for Einstein now, but many of them were to say that from 1925—the year he made his final statistical contribution to quantum research—on, he did not make another important discovery in physics. Einstein himself had the feeling that he was being retired.

"I already have more reputation than a person needs," he

commented in 1927 to the American physicist, Arthur Holly Compton. "I am happy to take my place among the routine workers in science."

Early in 1928, Einstein went to the Davos valley in Switzerland to lecture on physics to the young tubercular patients at the sanitarium there. On the train, he felt unusually weak and lethargic. He had been on the move for months—to Geneva and Paris for League meetings and to Leyden and Brussels for scientific discussions. Only a few weeks before, he had rushed to Holland to attend the funeral of his friend Lorentz. In a graveside address, Einstein had described Lorentz as "the greatest and noblest man of our times." The bearded old man, who for decades had been a "Mr. Chips" to young physicists, meant more to Einstein than anyone else. Lorentz had shown him how a genius should act as a human being—never try to dominate others, simply try to be of use to them.

Einstein was thinking about Lorentz on the train to Davos. Lorentz and death. His mysterious stomach pains were bothering him again. He was very short of breath. For weeks he had not eaten a decent meal. His physical condition was so much on his mind that he prefaced his lecture at the sanitarium with a little speech about the danger of brooding about sickness.

A few days later, in the resort valley of Engadine, he collapsed. Doctors diagnosed the trouble as acute enlargement of the heart. Einstein was in a state of exhaustion. He would have to stay in bed for at least three months. Elsa came down to Switzerland and took her husband back to Berlin by easy stages. Then she put him to bed and declared tobacco and pencil and paper out of bounds. She also hired a brisk young German woman, Helen Dukas, to handle his mail as his full-time secretary. Elsa's daughter Ilse, who had done this earlier, was now married to a young German journalist named Rudolf Kayser. Margot Einstein's time was occupied with her painting and sculpturing. She was soon to be married to Dmitri Maria-noff, a Russian writer.

Einstein was a boyish patient. A group of Jewish students was allowed to visit him one day on condition they did not worry him with their problems. After they had gone, Elsa found equations scrawled all over the white sheet.

A young physicist, Leo Szilard, helped Einstein relax by suggesting the idea of a pump using liquid metals. They invented a workable model and took out a patent, but nobody seemed interested.

Hans Albert came to see his father often. He regarded him as odd in many ways, but he liked him. Young Einstein was an engineer with a German company and married now. He always remembered his father's advice on the eve of his wedding: "Don't get married." Then Einstein explained that Hans Albert and his wife would only get separated later, so it wasn't worth the trouble.

Now, a year later, Einstein had more paternal advice.

"All right, you're married. But don't have any children."

"Why not?" young Albert—he was rarely called Hans—wanted to know.

"It makes divorce so much more complicated," Einstein said.

Later, when children did arrive and Albert remained very

happily married, Einstein grumbled: "I don't understand it. I don't think you're my son."

But to friends it seemed that father and son were too much alike, at least in some ways. Albert was much more decisive than his father, but both shared the same independent spirit. Frequently, they argued and Einstein said he wanted nothing more to do with Hans Albert. Mileva, who understood them both, always brought them together again.

Zangger, about the only other person who knew all the family foibles, was available to the boys when they needed a substitute father. There was the time when Albert wrote a mathematical thesis for his doctor of philosophy degree. The subject was somewhat out of his own field and he was sure Einstein would be pleased. Later he showed the thesis to Zangger, who read it with interest, then asked if Einstein was aware of it. Albert nodded. Zangger smiled: "I'll tell you what he said. He pointed out a certain passage and said, 'You could have said it a little better here.'" Actually, those were Einstein's exact words. He never wanted to appear a "softie."

Einstein had a different relationship with his younger son. Edward was more sensitive and needed encouragement. He had started a medical course and Einstein warmly approved. Edward was passionately fond of his father and wanted desperately to live up to him. At the same time, he felt rejected because Einstein had left the family. And he feared he would never be a worthy son to a genius. He had studied hard all his young life—science, literature, philosophy, medicine—and he had a vast range of knowledge stored in his mind. But he could never add anything of his own. There was not one creative cell in his whole being. He knew this and it depressed him. Once he had even copied a fine piece of writing out of a book and presented it as his own. He wanted to show his father that he could create. He was discovered, of course. Nobody seemed able to help him adjust to this flaw in his mind. It was no comfort to him to know that most people in the world had the same trouble. His only answer was that most people in the world did not have Einstein for a father.

The longer Einstein stayed in bed during his 1928 sickness, the more morose he became. He worried about Edward and he worried about death. He did not fear death. He was just concerned that it might take him before he had enough money in the bank to care for his family and before he had finished his work.

Several doctors examined him, but it was a high-priced "society" doctor named Plesch who came up with the right answer. He suspected the wall of Einstein's heart was inflamed. He prescribed a salt-free diet. Within weeks, Einstein was completely cured and was able to get back wholeheartedly to his physics.

His confinement had moved him off the public stage a little. Now there were fewer demands on him to sit on committees and to write messages for various causes.

Alone in his attic, he toiled over gravitation and electricity. By Christmas, he was working on a new geometry that seemed to answer problems in both fields. He would not have gone to a pacifist rally even if it had been held just around the corner. He was completely gripped. By early January, he thought he had it—a block of equations that locked together like a finished crossword puzzle. He saw it as a reasonable marriage of the laws of gravitation and electromagnetism, founded on general Relativity. Its weakness was that it could not be tested by any experiment. It was purely theoretical and purely mathematical. Einstein realized he might be on the wrong track, but this first version of the unified field theory was worth publishing. He had several years of his life invested in the theory. Indirectly, it had cost him a family. The Prussian Academy sent it to the printers.

Newspapermen learned about the theory days before it was published. Local newspapers were lukewarm. They thought Einstein had had too much publicity. But the men from the Berlin bureaus of foreign newspapers crowded into Haberlandstrasse by the carload. It was impossible to find a parking place along the street. Photographers kept a twenty-four-hour vigil outside Einstein's apartment house. But Einstein would not come out and Elsa would not let anybody in. There was only one exception—the man from *The New York Times*. It had been Einstein's favorite newspaper since his visit to New York in 1921. Einstein really wanted to know what all the fuss was about. "It's your new theory," said the reporter. The physicist struck his brow with the heel of his hand. "My God," he said. And he shook his head from side to side in utter amazement.

The Prussian Academy would not release the theory in advance of general publication on January 30. Then, it was explained, reporters could purchase the paper for the price of one mark (twenty-five cents). A professor briefed the press only on the object of the theory. Several reporters, realizing the historic value of Einstein's long-hand version of the theory, offered thousands of marks for the original. They were too late. Wesleyan University in Connecticut had already contracted to buy it.

The furor was building. Correspondents cabled their home offices. How much copy did they want on the theory? Most of the European papers preferred a "lay" explanation plus any understandable direct quotes from the article itself.

However, American editors saw it differently. Einstein had apparently discovered the equations God used to keep the universe running. So they wanted everything. The New York *Evening Post* wanted a picture radioed of the first page of the text. The newspaper's correspondent said it would be very costly—Berlin to London, then London to New York. It had never been done before. "We want that picture," the *Post* cabled abruptly. This was the era when newspapers were alive —exciting because of the way in which they got the news as well as for the stories themselves.

On the big day the New York *Herald Tribune* did the most heroic job. Berlin bureau chief John Elliott picked up the Einstein theory at 2 p.m., the second it was issued. It was a six-page jumble of mathematical formulae. After getting it translated into English, Elliott cabled the entire theory. Where possible, he changed symbols into words. He sent an advance code to New York warning that words like "oblique" should be symbolized. "Raised" meant that the letter or number following it should be upper index. "Sub" meant lower index. In New York, the deciphering was done by a team of physicists from Columbia University. They started in the morning, as soon as Elliott's copy began coming through, and it was past midnight before the theory was ready for the paper.

New Yorkers, along with Londoners and Romans and Rio de Janeirons, studied the theory over breakfast. They were delighted. It was pure Einstein. They did not understand the first thing about it, and they knew nobody else did either.

The New York Times made a valiant last attempt to bring Einstein down to earth. He agreed to write a simple explanation of the theory. It was published early in February. There was much nodding of heads for a week or two until an honest reader wrote in saying he still did not understand Einstein and would the *Times* please summarize the theory in a few concise sentences.

Cheerfully, the *Times* replied in an editorial: "It is necessary to state with becoming modesty that the editorial staff of the *Times* does not, unfortunately, include any of the twelve men in all the world who alone understand Einstein. A larger number, to be sure, profess to do so; but in their confidential moments they will confess to sympathy with the hobo in a public park turning with a newspaper in his hand to a neighbor and admitting, 'I don't get this Einstein guy at all.' "

Much less publicized was the fact that most of the great physicists in the world—men like Niels Bohr, Paul Dirac, Louis de Broglie, Wolfgang Pauli, Ernest Rutherford, even Paul Ehrenfest—knew exactly what Einstein was trying to do. But they did not sympathize with his new work because it ignored the quantum theories. Einstein's theory certainly did not stem from quantum and apparently it did not lead to it, either.

135

Later, the very preliminary nature of the theory became fully evident. Undismayed, Einstein set out to rebuild it.

The public cared nothing for the scientific discussion. People were charmed by the modest genius whose mind had conquered the universe. He was a man to enjoy. Nobody envied him for his brain, his wife or his money. Nobody spoiled his image as the symbol of the extreme in scientific jargon. Anybody who claimed to comprehend Einstein could be shut up with two words—explain Relativity.

In a belated move to show that Germany, too, was aware of Einstein's greatness, the Berlin Municipal Council announced, in sugary releases to the newspapers, that the city would present a country villa to its "distinguished son." The council found records of a fine, untenanted house in a grove of trees near a little lake. The house and several acres surrounding it were owned by the city. Newspaper photographers located the house and pictures were published. Elsa Einstein was excited about the gift. She went to the lake but could not get inside the house. People were living there.

Embarrassed councilors discovered that another "distinguished son" had already been given the house. Never mind, a second villa would be built on the property for Einstein. No, you don't, complained the squatter in Villa Number One. He produced a document in which the council had promised never to build another structure on the place.

The council was becoming a laughingstock. Hurriedly, it selected still another piece of land for the Einstein house. Elsa checked this one, too. She was almost run off the property by the owner. All right, decided the councilors, let the Einsteins pick their own plot of land and the city would buy it for them. To save further confusion, they could build and pay for their own house. Elsa found an ideal spot at the end of a dirt road by the sleepy little village of Caputh, near Potsdam. It was close to a lake. Albert could enjoy sailing, one of his greatest pleasures. Elsa wrote to the council, describing the land of her choice.

At a supposedly routine council meeting to vote on the gift, the conservative members objected. Sullenly they said Einstein did not deserve the land. The meeting adjourned before a vote could be taken. Einstein had played a passive role during the whole contretemps but when this latest development was reported to him, he wrote immediately to the mayor: "Human life is very short, but the authorities work very slowly. I feel therefore that my life is too short for me to adapt myself to your methods . . . I decline the gift."

This was just part of the uproar surrounding the approach of Einstein's fiftieth birthday in March, 1929. The reporters were back in droves on Haberlandstrasse, all asking for an elucidation of the unified field theory and any other birthday messages he might have. Publishers hounded him to name his own price for his life story. Hair-brained inventors crowded the sidewalk with plans for rocket ships. The mail men had the worst of it. Gifts arrived from all over the world—pipes, telescopes, books, four violins, hand-knitted sweaters, and a case of champagne.

Einstein began to hope he would never reach fifty. When March 14 did come, he sneaked out of his house before dawn, scuttled into a limousine sent for him by a rich friend, and hid

EINSTEIN, PROFILE OF THE MAN

out in the gardener's cottage on that friend's big country estate.

Elsa and her daughters joined him for a birthday supper after detouring miles out of their way to escape a few persistent reporters.

Only one reporter found the cottage. Timidly he knocked on the door. Elsa answered it and told the man to go away. Einstein called in a strained voice from the other room:

"Tell the young man I don't need any publicity."

CHAPTER 8

TRAGEDY IN ZURICH

Einstein's unified field theory, which nobody understood, started a religious controversy.

In New York, the Rev. Dr. Henry Howard told a Presbyterian congregation that Einstein was proving the very thing guessed at in St. Paul's synthesis—"that all things are one." A Methodist minister preached that Jesus, the Jew of the first century, had shown a new earth. Einstein, the Jew of the twentieth century, had shown a new heaven.

Cardinal O'Connell of Boston took the opposite approach. He said Einstein's theories were "befogged speculation, producing universal doubt about God and his creation." *Osservatore Romano,* in an editorial reflecting Vatican views, noted that Cardinal O'Connell was right to denounce Einstein's theories because they "tended to cut off faith in God from human life." The editorial added: "This is authentic atheism even if it is camouflaged as cosmic pantheism."

Rabbi Herbert Goldstein of New York was annoyed at

139

these attacks. He cabled Einstein a blunt question: "Do you believe in God?"

Einstein replied immediately: "I believe in Spinoza's God who reveals himself in the harmony of all that exists, not in a God who concerns himself with the fate and actions of men."

The reply satisfied Goldstein, who now declared Einstein a deeply religious man. But the statement angered many other people. The Jewish magazine *Reflex,* published in Chicago, suggested sarcastically that Goldstein might like to sanctify Einstein. In an editorial that gathered force as it went along, the magazine said:

"From a strictly religious point of view the great scientist is not a Jew at all, but Judaism is not belief and spirituality alone. It is also blood. Therefore no matter what Einstein believes, he is still a Jew . . . Spinozism may or may not be a sort of religiosity, but surely it is not Jewish religiosity and is the antithesis of religious Judaism. It is for this reason that Spinoza was excommunicated. The excommunication is valid to the present day. Spinoza was excommunicated for the very good religious reason . . . that he denied the personality of God and tried to chain God to His own laws. According to the Jewish conception of God, He is free and not bound by His own laws. Spinoza's God may not bother about the fate of the individual but He is not free, either, and if He wanted to direct the destiny of Man, He could not possibly do so because He is chained to the immutable laws of nature. This, in the eyes of the pious ones, is worse than plain atheism. It is pure blasphemy . . ."

Einstein agreed that this criticism fitted his non-belief to a point, but he did not like being called an atheist. In a conversation with the Hindu poet and mystic, Rabindranath Tagore, in Berlin, he indicated his rather special way of looking at life.

Tagore: "The reality of the world depends on human consciousness. It is a human universe."

Einstein: "I agree with this conception in regard to beauty but not to truth."

Tagore: "Why not? Truth is realized through Man."

Einstein: "Scientific truth must be conceived as a truth that is valid and independent of humanity. I cannot prove that I am right in this, but that is my religion."

In a long talk with author George Sylvester Viereck, Einstein spelled out his beliefs in very simple language.

"In the first place," he said, "the human mind, no matter how highly trained, is not capable of grasping the universe. We are like a little child entering a huge library. The walls are covered to the ceiling with books in many different tongues. The child knows that someone must have written those books. It does not know who or how. It does not understand the languages in which they are written. The child notes a definite plan in the arrangement of the books—a mysterious order which it does not comprehend, but only dimly suspects. That, it seems to me, is the attitude of the human mind towards God. And because I believe this, I am not an atheist."

Viereck asked Einstein if he believed that Jesus had existed.

"Unquestionably," said Einstein. "No one can read the Gospels without feeling the central presence of Jesus. His personality is in every word. No myth is filled with such life."

How did Einstein view his own accomplishments?

He claimed credit for nothing. Everything was determined, the beginning as well as the end, by forces over which Man had no control. It was determined for the insect as well as for the star. Human beings, vegetables or cosmic dust—they all danced to a mysterious tune.

"My own career," he said, "was undoubtedly determined, not by my own will, but by various factors over which I have no control—primarily those mysterious glands in which nature prepares the very essence of life . . ."

People studied Einstein's statements with keen interest. He knew more about the cosmos than any man in history. Perhaps he had learned something new about God. Churchmen, however, assured their congregations that Einstein knew no more about God than the most humble shepherd. His denial of the existence of a personal God and his denial of human free will should not be taken seriously, they said.

The impromptu religious discussion—Einstein versus The Rest—brought Einstein, the man, into more accurate focus.

While nearly everyone else was inclined to think of himself in the context of the world and his own times, Einstein thought in terms of the universe and eternity. In Einstein's picture, the individual had very little significance. His existence was "hardly more than a fragment of a second in the life of the earth." Many people attributed Einstein's apparent serenity to his satisfaction with what he saw as his own infinitesmal role in eternity. He did not need the promise of another life in the "hereafter" to keep him happy.

In spite of this outlook, a passionate sense of social justice and social responsibility had urged Albert Einstein into the human fray in 1919. Now, ten years later and more famous than ever, he was again moved to take an active part in social reform. This was his fourth dimension and he did not quite understand it. He became interested in the League of Nations, pacifist groups, civil rights organizations and Zionism. These activities helped him forget that he was slowing down in his real work.

Einstein indicated his readiness to involve himself in human affairs around this time when a German businessman wrote suggesting that feuding between countries might be curbed by international meetings of war veterans on World War I battlefields.

"A wonderful idea," said Einstein. "Please call on me for any help."

Europe was outwardly calm, but nationalism was as rampant as always. Most countries were secretly building up arsenals. Einstein preached disarmament, unilaterally if necessary. A country with no defenses would be vulnerable, but the risk must be taken. Dumping weapons was the best way to dramatize the human struggle for the eradication of all wars. Einstein was guardedly optimistic about the future of Europe. Germany, the most aggressive of the nations, was slowly losing her bitterness and arrogance. This was due mostly to Foreign Minister Gustav Stresemann. He had negotiated reparations down to a very reasonable level and then met them conscientiously. Stresemann also got Germany into the League of Nations. And with him virtually running the government the other countries were prepared to accept Germany as a respectable republican voice in the world.

In the summer of 1929, Einstein felt sure enough about the future to start building his vacation cottage at Caputh. On their property was a knoll, and for this Albert and Elsa designed a simple timber house with big windows to fit. The approach was terraced because Elsa wanted flower gardens. Builders had the house up in a month. "It was all glass and wood," said a friend. "It looked incongruously modern in such an old-fashioned village."

Einstein loved the place. The nearest railroad station was miles away and the roads were too poor to tempt the curious. Affluent friends presented him with a new sailboat to go with the house. It was a gleaming mahogany craft more than twenty feet long. It had an enclosed cockpit containing a toilet. Einstein had never seen a toilet on a sailboat before; he was delighted. But he felt that the boat itself was too fancy. To be sure, he enjoyed sailing in friends' flashy boats and visiting their swank homes. Yet every time he himself spent money on luxuries or was given something expensive, he was plagued with a guilt complex. The money would be far more useful to a good charity, he protested. His previous boat was a leaky little thing called *Lisa;* he had bought her fourth-hand. Everyone else called her *Drunken Lisa.* Since *Lisa* was virtually a wreck, Einstein accepted the new mahogany boat in spite of his misgivings.

Hans Albert, who had inherited his father's love for sailing, visited Caputh to help put the boat through its paces. He was pleased to find his father virtually unchanged. Out on the lake, Einstein started to talk about the field theory. He became more and more engrossed, lounging back with the tiller and mainsail rope in his hand. The breeze was high and the lake was narrowing but Einstein talked on. A few yards from a rocky bank, Albert interrupted his father: "Very interesting. But if you don't mind, we're nearly aground."

The summer was glorious. The fall was disastrous.

The ruin started with the death of Gustav Stresemann, on October 3, at the age of fifty-one. He had worked himself to death. On October 24, the New York stock market collapsed with a bang that set off a chain reaction around the world. And all through the month, Arabs killed Jews in a bloodthirsty protest against Jewish colonization of Palestine. A group of Arab fanatics was out to sabotage Zionism. Already there was talk of limiting Jewish migration to Palestine.

Einstein wrote an impassioned plea for justice and distributed it to European and American newspapers . . .

"Our generation has seen no national effort of such spiritual intensity and such heroic devotion as that which the Jews have displayed during the last ten years in a work of peace in Palestine . . . Is it not bewildering that, after all this, brutal massacres by a fanaticized mob can destroy all appreciation of the Jewish effort in Palestine and lead to a demand for the repeal of the solemn pledges of official support and protection?"

Einstein wrote nearly one thousand words, pointing out that Jews had paid for every acre of land they settled, that Jews and Arabs had shown they could live happily as neighbors if the gangsters were driven away, that the ideals of Zionism deserved world support.

The British took note of "Dr. Einstein's remarks." An investigation was being conducted.

In the months that followed, Einstein spoke loudly and often about Zionism, pacifism, liberalism. Nobody took any notice. In Germany, Adolf Hitler's Nazi party, long under a cloud, gained support now in direct proportion to the growth of unemployment. The Reichstag voted once to uphold Stresemann's policies, but after that, nationalism forged ahead.

Again, a disillusioned Einstein retreated into science. He persuaded a brilliant Austrian mathematician, Walter Mayer, to become his assistant because he needed new mathematical ideas to develop his field theory. Apparently Einstein had exhausted all the text-book knowledge. And now as he got deeper into his new work, his statements and letters about human affairs became shorter and crustier.

To a group of churchmen urging him to attend a peace rally in Berne, he wrote: "If I had been able to address your congress, I would have said that in the course of history, the priests have been responsible for much strife and war among human beings; they have a great deal to atone for . . ."

Once more he resigned from the League of Nations' Committee on Intellectual Co-operation because it seemed to him ineffectual. In his view the League had not lived up to its promises to support minorities like Jews, and to resist chauvinistic trends in education.

But it was not so easy for Einstein to cut himself off from the world this time. In the early summer of 1930, he received a long and vindictive letter from his son Edward. More followed. Edward accused him of putting a shadow over his life. He had sired him, then deserted him. The letters were hysterical and fierce. Edward said he hated his father.

Bewildered and hurt, Einstein went to Zurich to reason with the boy. He found Mileva distraught. She said she needed Albert's help desperately. Edward had suffered a breakdown. She could not learn the cause. Perhaps worry over examinations at the university was responsible. A tragic love affair was also suspected. Whatever the reason, Edward, now twenty-one, had had an intense fit of melancholia. The family realized that Edward had long had intense and contradictory feelings toward his father—feelings of love, even worship, curiously mixed with a sense of rejection and personal inadequacy. It now seemed that his confused mind held nothing but hate for Einstein. Oddly enough, Edward realized that his mind was sick. But he just could not shake off the depression. His life was ruined and he blamed his father.

Although Einstein still distrusted psychiatry, he sent Edward to the best psychoanalysts in Switzerland. The young man's condition only grew worse there. He was taken to Vienna, then the world center of psychiatry, but still without result. He was neurotic, but not violent, and in the end Mileva insisted on keeping her son at home. The personal problems between herself and Albert suddenly seemed unimportant, and Mileva no longer brooded about them. The mysterious grudge she had held for more than twenty-five years was forgotten. Hans Albert, visiting Zurich, found that Edward's tragedy had drawn his father and mother close together again.

Ironically, Edward's fantastic store of knowledge actually prevented his cure and destined him to a life on the edge of society. He knew as much about psychoanalysis as any of his doctors. When they asked him questions or made him perform

147

physical tests, he knew precisely what they were trying to discover. As a result, his inner mind was forever sealed to them.

Shortly after Edward's breakdown, Einstein was asked to summarize his philosophy of life. He started off with a paragraph that reflected the part of his heart he revealed only to his family . . .

"How strange is the lot of us mortals. Each of us is here for a brief sojourn; for what purpose we know not, though we sometimes think we sense it. But without deeper reflection, we know from daily life that we exist for other people—first of all for those upon whose smiles and well-being our own happiness is wholly dependent . . ."

Einstein's rollicking laugh was not heard at Caputh that summer or fall. He aged in a matter of months. Crisscross lines of pain deepened under his eyes. His hair was whiter, his mustache grayer. Nevertheless, he and Mayer were digging into physics' toughest problems. The papers they turned out were interesting but not notable.

Elsa told her friend Antonina Vallentin, later an Einstein biographer, that Albert's sorrow over Edward was eating him up. Her husband had always tried to stay above personal worries, but this had hit him hard.

In October, Einstein visited England to lecture on Relativity and to make a speech in London to raise funds for Jewish refugees from eastern Europe. He got back to Berlin in time to vote for the Social Democrats in the national election. His party won, but the Nazis rocketed from their previous twelve seats to one hundred seven seats—the second largest majority. At the other end of the ticket, the Communists scored seventy-seven seats.

Einstein saw that Germany was headed for political chaos. Banks were failing and lines in front of soup kitchens were growing longer and longer. He was powerless to help. Hungry men were not interested in idealism. In his own life, he was unsure of his next step in physics and he was in constant torment over Edward.

"The winter here can bring nothing but sadness," Elsa wrote Miss Vallentin. "We intend to go away for a long time."

Einstein accepted an invitation from Professor Robert Millikan to spend the winter as a visiting professor at the California Institute of Technology in Pasadena. There was the added incentive of attending seminars at the Mount Wilson Observatory which had become world famous for astrophysical research. Lorentz had spent two winters in Pasadena and Paul Ehrenfest had been there, too. Both had told Einstein of its scientific importance.

Although nearly ten years had passed since he first visited New York, the tumult was still vivid in Einstein's memory. He was in no mood to face it again. But he could not find a boat that bypassed the place and so had to settle for the *Belgenland* which called at New York and Havana and then went on through the Panama Canal to San Diego.

"We have five days in New York," he grumbled to Berlin reporters before leaving home in late November with Elsa and his secretary, Helen Dukas. "I am seriously thinking of remaining aboard all that time. Facing the cameramen on arrival and submitting to a crossfire of the newspapermen's questions is enough of an ordeal, but that's over in a few minutes. Then the real difficulties begin. I abhor crowds, invitations and speeches."

In truth, Einstein liked a certain amount of public recognition—it had become part of his life—but New York did carry things to ridiculous extremes.

The trip started badly. The Red Star Line allotted him a three-room suite and two personal stewards for the price of his first-class ticket. "This is awful," he said. "I feel like an indirect exploiter of labor." Elsa hushed him by saying the steamship people would be hurt if he made a fuss. "But I want to be treated like anybody else," he protested.

Helen Dukas had heard this plea from Einstein so often that she dreamt about it one night. A burglar broke into the Einstein house and lined up everybody against a wall, demanding that they empty their pockets. When the burglar reached Einstein he said: "Not you, Professor. I couldn't take anything from Einstein." The professor said: "Yes, please. I want to be treated like anybody else." He then reached into his pocket and handed a dime to the burglar.

The voyage across the Atlantic relaxed the weary scientist. He played his violin several times with the ship's band and graciously posed for pictures with the other passengers. But he charged a dollar for an autograph—it was a way to raise money for a Jewish refugee welfare fund.

Before the *Belgenland* was properly into New York harbor, he saw the reporters swarming aboard from small boats. Running to his suite, he locked all the doors. But after fifteen minutes he came out and suffered his press conference. He even appeared jovial. Actually, he dearly wanted to please everyone. He wanted to say and do what was expected of him. At that period of his life, he acted less and less on impulse. People who had known him in his gay young days in Switzerland regretted the change. They preferred the jocular Einstein. In 1930, they felt, he worried too much about what people might think of him.

When he arrived in New York, it was apparent that he was eager to hurry on to Pasadena and talk science. But in a radio broadcast message, he said that America was the bulwark of the democratic way of life and it should help defeat the menace of militarism and that he was "eagerly looking forward to renewing old friendships and to broadening my understanding [of America] in the light of what I shall see and learn while I am among you."

Two days later, he was taken to see his sculptured head mounted, along with those of the great sages of the past, on the wall of Manhattan's Riverside Church. He was pleased that a Jew had been honored by a Protestant church. He added: "I must not say or write anything silly that would spoil this honor." Constantly, he kept reminding himself to set a good example.

Significantly, Einstein's most memorable speech in years was delivered in New York—extemporaneously. He had been asked to say a few words at a meeting of pacifists in a hotel convention room. It was a genteel group and Einstein had grown tired of platitudes. So he got up and said it was time for deeds—not words. True pacifists should not only refuse to answer conscription calls, they should announce publicly that they would not take up arms under any circumstances . . .

"If only two per cent of those assigned to military service should announce their refusal to fight . . . governments would be powerless. They would not dare send such a large number of people to jail."

Pacifist writer Alfred Lief said the people were stirred. He wrote: "Pale, gentle, almost melancholy, Einstein stood at the microphone as a presence more forceful than a grim marine with bayonet fixed."

Liberal-minded students on American college campuses affectionately dubbed him "Two Per Cent Einstein." Within weeks, the battle cry of pacifists all over the world was, "Two Per Cent to Glory."

Einstein was applauded at the Metropolitan Opera, cheered at a Hanukkah festival, chased in his limousine, called incessantly on the telephone. Thirty-five New Yorkers claimed to be his cousin. A Wall Streeter was arrested for advertising that Einstein had approved his mathematical system for beating the stock market. A Viennese professor named Kwartin ran a small ad in the *Times* saying he could teach Relativity in fifteen lessons "at low cost." Fritz Kreisler and Einstein posed with their violins. Toscanini and Einstein discussed Mozart. John D. Rockefeller, Jr., and Einstein argued economics. Helen Keller put her fingers on Einstein's lips and the two chatted for twenty minutes.

Then, as the *Belgenland* weighed anchor, Einstein told the farewell throng: "I am leaving New York with a sense of new spiritual and mental enrichment." But in his diary he wrote: "I'm dead."

Einstein thought it was a wild exaggeration when a newspaper described him as the most famous man in the world. He reconsidered at Colon, the noisy town at the entrance to the Panama Canal. He and Elsa were jogging along a rutted plantation road in a pony cart, miles from anywhere, when a Latino in a soiled white suit stepped from a little shack and ordered the driver to halt. He bowed to the Einsteins with a sweep of his sombrero. *"Buenas tardes,* Professor," he said. "Forgive me, but I have heard of your theory of Relativity and I want to say that I don't agree with it." Then he stepped back and waved the cart on.

California intrigued Einstein. First, it was the number of cars. Then it was the supermarkets—"everyone serves himself and pays for the things he has gathered in his basket"—and finally, it was Hollywood. Producers and actors staged a banquet in his honor. All the supercolossal Hollywood adjectives were used by speakers to describe their guest and Einstein thought they were spoofing. He responded simply: "Thank you, but I'd have to be crazy to believe all those things, and I know I'm not crazy." After the banquet he was taken to a special screening of *All Quiet on the Western Front,* based on Erich Maria Remarque's novel. The book had been published in Germany the year before, but the film had been banned. Einstein promised the producers to fight the ban when he returned to Berlin. He said the picture was the most powerful indictment against war he had ever seen.

In Hollywood, a meeting was arranged between Einstein and Charlie Chaplin. Einstein wanted to learn about comedy and film-making. Chaplin wanted to talk about socialism and the world depression. Later, Chaplin asked for Einstein's photograph. The physicist signed it: "To Charles Chaplin, the great economist." Einstein reversed the usual system—he gave his autographed picture to the stars.

To the practiced Hollywood eye, he had a magnificent character face. At least one producer offered him a job as an actor. His scientific friends were shocked at the "insult." Einstein himself was not offended. As far as he was concerned, entertainment was a fine profession. He liked to dramatize his lectures and he enjoyed playing his violin for people. Now if the producer had suggested a role along those lines . . .

Einstein spent two months at Pasadena. He learned a great deal about the universe there. Californians thought he was joking when he said he was going back to school, but he meant it.

At Mount Wilson Observatory, he studied galaxies millions of light years away from earth—great clusters of stars and suns and clouds wheeling around in Einsteinian gravitational fields. He heard American astronomers discuss their latest observations and speculations about the Andromeda galaxy, seven hundred thousand light years away and nearest neighbor in space to the Milky Way galaxy of which our earth is one tiny member. Walter Adams and Charles St. John lectured about the sun's atmosphere—nine thousand miles deep compared with the one hundred-mile depth of the earth's atmosphere— and its layers of ionized calcium, hydrogen, helium and other gases. Yet the mighty sun was not even the center of the Milky Way, merely a husky outrider with its own little system of planets and stars.

154

Einstein noted a marked lack of egotism among the Mount Wilson scientists.

Many years earlier, he had theorized that the universe was four-dimensional, finite and spherical. It was like a giant balloon. The over-all effect of the great conglomeration of moons and stars and other matter, each producing a curvature in the space-time fabric, was a universe that curved back on itself. The arrangement of matter remained the same, each piece traveling only its local route.

In 1930, by observation and test astronomers had proven that distant nebulae were receding from telescopic view. The universe was not static after all. Einstein checked all this work at Mount Wilson and was convinced. "The shift of nebulae has smashed my old construction of the universe like a hammer blow . . . The only possibility now is to say that the universe was originally static. It lasted in that state for a while, then became unstable and expansion started. But who would believe it?"

However, the incredible notion of an expanding universe became widely accepted. The big balloon was swelling larger and larger. Einstein's old friend, Arthur Eddington, caused a sensation when he discovered an article, dated 1927, in an obscure journal, giving the idea mathematical support. The author was a Belgian Jesuit, Abbé Georges Lemaître, who advanced the theory that the universe originated from a huge, fantastically heavy "primeval atom." This atom exploded thousands of millions of years ago and produced the universe. Even today, the force of the explosion had not abated. The universe was still being scattered.

Early in March, 1931, Einstein had to leave all this excitement, but he promised to return to Mount Wilson the next winter. Before he departed, he lectured California Tech students about the improper use of applied science. "In war," he said, "it has given us the means to poison and mutilate each other. In peace, it has made our lives hurried and uncertain. It has made men into slaves of machinery. They complete their long, monotonous day's work in disgust." Einstein said he did not like to speak this way, but it was the truth. "Just consider a quite uncivilized Indian," he added. "I hardly think his experience is less rich and happy than that of the average civilized man. There lies a deep meaning in the fact that the children of all civilized countries are so fond of playing Indian."

The Indians themselves may have heard of these remarks, for when Einstein's eastbound train stopped near the Grand Canyon, the Hopi tribe greeted the professor enthusiastically and named him "Great Relative."

In Chicago, Einstein made a speech about pacifism from the rear platform of his train like any campaigning politician. The next day he repeated the speech in New York, emphasizing that the farcical disarmament talks in Geneva made it imperative for people to take matters into their own hands and denounce military service and arms factories.

"Nothing that I can do or say will change the structure of the universe," he told one interviewer. "But maybe, by raising my voice, I can help the greatest of all causes—goodwill among men and peace on earth."

Hours before he boarded his ship for the return trip to Germany, President Herbert Hoover wired that his visit had been "gratifying to the American people." Out in Hollywood, however, Will Rogers said that Einstein was a great guy, but a little impractical. "Asking Europe to disarm is like asking a man in Chicago to give up his life insurance," he drawled.

CHAPTER 9

FREUD TO EINSTEIN

In the spring of 1931, Professor Emil Gumbel of Heidelberg University was hanged in effigy by students. Other professors looked on with approval. Nobody came to Gumbel's lectures. The windows of his home were smashed. He was beaten up. His life was constantly threatened. Gumbel's crime was that of writing pacifist pamphlets which documented the secret re-armament of Germany. When the violence started, Gumbel replied with even more damning pamphlets.

Einstein followed the proceedings with a sense of doom. The Gumbel case was plainly a symptom of a new reign of terror. In a letter to the *Berliner Tageblatt*, he said: "What shall become of a people who brutally persecute men like Gumbel and whose leaders offer no opposition to the common mob? . . . If things go on like this, we shall arrive at a Fascist regime of tyranny."

This, of course, is exactly what Hitler had in mind as 1931 progressed. Millions of men were out of work and the Nazi

Party incited them to join its ranks by promising a new and powerful Fatherland in which the defeatist cult of liberalism would be trampled forever. Nazi candidates were winning elections all over Germany because Storm Troopers stood by to harass voters and to frighten opponents with fists and gun butts. Already, many leading German industrialists had decided to throw their financial support behind the Nazis.

Einstein fought a delaying action. He issued a stream of statements pleading for the preservation of the German Republic, internationalism, peace. He told Elsa he would dramatize his cause by renouncing his German citizenship and then holding up the Nazi policies to world examination. But he kept changing his mind about this. One day he got as far as writing a letter to the directors of the Prussian Academy, telling them of his intention. Later he tore it up.

Then he went to Oxford University as a visiting professor, and spent as much time there espousing pacifism as he did talking science.

Intuitively he smelled war. He told the British parliamentarian, Fenner Brockway, that peace societies should oppose all war without qualifications and insist on complete disarmament by their own governments, whatever other nations might do.

This was the stand of an organization called War Resisters' International whose membership was drawn from fifty-six countries. Einstein became a driving force in the group. He told fellow pacifists to get off their knees and fight or leave the cause altogether.

"This is not the time for temporizing," he said in his most

forceful speech since he became "Two Per Cent Einstein."
"You are either for war or against war. If you are for war, then
go ahead and encourage science, finance, industry, religion
and labor to exert all their power for the arms build-up, to
make weapons as deadly as possible. If you are against war,
then challenge everyone to resist it to the limits of his capacity.
I ask everyone who reads these words to make this grave and
final decision.

"Let this generation be the one to take the greatest step forward ever made in the history of mankind. Let it leave to
future generations the inestimable heritage of a world from
which the brutalities of war have been banished forever. We
can do this if we are determined. It merely requires that all
who hate war shall have the courage to say that they will not
tolerate war.

"I appeal to all men and women, whether they be eminent or
humble, to declare, before the World Disarmament Conference convenes at Geneva next February, that they will hence-
forth refuse to give assistance to any war or preparations for
war. I ask them to inform their governments in writing of that
decision and to confirm the decision by advising me about it.

"I shall look for many thousands of responses to this appeal.
They should be addressed to me at the headquarters of the
War Resisters' International . . . I have authorized the es-
tablishment of the Einstein War Resisters' International Fund.
Contributions to this fund should be sent to . . ."

Einstein had never gone this far before. He had committed
himself to a project that could take up most of his time. Close
friends wondered how he would extricate himself when he

started to move ahead on his physics again. It never came to a choice. The world loved and respected Einstein as a scientific genius, but apparently not as a statesman. The response to his appeal was insignificant. He swallowed his disappointment and shifted his attention to the unified field theory.

After working themselves into several blind alleys, Einstein and Mayer had found a new way to advance by using mathematical concepts worked out by a certain Professor Theodore Kaluza. These concepts were beyond the understanding of laymen, although Einstein breezily explained that they simply meant "introducing a vector of five components into the space-time continuum of four dimensions."

The fresh version of the unified field theory was completed at Caputh in October. Einstein told reporters it was a "definite advance in knowledge of the structure of physical space," but warned that it was by no means final. All this time, he still went nearly every day to his office at the Prussian Academy and attended the weekly seminars. Several of the professors there avoided his company now because of his reputation as a "radical." Often at the seminars, the seat on either side of him was left empty.

Nevertheless, he had a strange affinity for Berlin; he found it intellectually stimulating. Mileva and Hans Albert argued that he had done his most creative work in Switzerland, but he did not agree. For, even though shaken by Edward's illness, he still felt that he needed to keep remote from family responsibilities and to remain with an organization that paid him handsomely for pure research.

"I want to stay put," he told his older son. Yet Hans Albert knew his father well enough not to be surprised when he turned up a few days later in Austria, Holland or Belgium. He had invitations to lecture all over Europe. The only ones he would not consider were those from Russia. "They would try to use me for political propaganda," he said.

In Vienna, Einstein had a typical reception. After playing his usual game with reporters by traveling third class and by trying to escape through a freight exit at the station—a game he rather enjoyed, he was taken to the lecture hall by motor-cycle escort. Because the hall could not accommodate the audience, amplifiers were installed in the two adjacent rooms. Einstein was then signaled to proceed.

His lecture topics included Relativity, the unified field theory and the expanding universe. In the fall of 1931, at a Berlin public lecture, he attempted something a little lighter. "The times are so grave that everyone should try to cheer up his neighbor," he began. Then he spoke for two hours on why sand is solid when wet but muddy in water; why an airplane flies, and why tea leaves gather in the middle of the cup when the tea is stirred.

Brussels was one of his favorite towns. He had become friendly with King Albert and Queen Elizabeth and every time he visited the city he went to dinner at the palace and stayed for an evening of music. The Queen played second fiddle to Einstein's first in a string quartet. Elizabeth fascinated him. She had sent her children to public schools, she smoked cigarettes, she was a trained nurse and she had accepted the presidency of the Society for the Prevention of Venereal Disease.

He went to Brussels again in 1931 and stopped at a busy

tavern by the station to telephone Elizabeth. He wanted to suggest a musical session. He tried to phone her several times, but the line was always busy. He stamped around impatiently.

"Who are you trying to call?" asked the bartender.

"The King's," said Einstein.

"The King's?" said the bartender.

"Yes, King Albert's home, the royal residence," said Einstein.

Shaking his head, the bartender went back to serving his sober customers.

Einstein finally completed his call and spent the afternoon fiddling at "the King's." He stayed for dinner and later detailed the menu in a letter to Elsa—spinach, hard-boiled eggs, potatoes.

Early in December, the Einsteins again boarded a ship for California. This time they managed to get one that by-passed New York. A few days out, Albert was musing about the freedom of seagulls; then made another of his twenty-four-hour decisions.

"I decided today to give up my Berlin position and become a bird of passage for the rest of my life," he wrote in his diary. "Gulls are still escorting the ship, forever on the wing. They are my new colleagues."

At Pasadena, Einstein wanted to sink himself into his science studies. But his idealism was shocked by American indifference to the problems of Europe. This apathy was apparent both in newspapers and in conversation. He kept criticizing the attitude in speeches at banquets and meetings. He said it was ignoble . . .

"America is not without responsibility for the difficulties that beset Europe. By ruthlessly pressing her claims, she in fact hastens the economic and moral decline of Europe; she has contributed to the Balkanization of Europe and must, therefore, share in the responsibility for the breakdown of political morality and the emergence of the spirit of revenge which feeds on despair . . . Let us be outspoken and straightforward: the disarmament conference opening in Geneva presents the final opportunity to you, no less than to us, to preserve the best that humanity has produced. It is toward America, the strongest and, relatively speaking, healthiest among the nations, that the eyes and hopes of all mankind are directed."

His conviction that the Geneva conference was Europe's "last stand" had grown over many months. He spoke with passion and urgency, yet nobody seemed to take much notice. He was infuriated; as Elsa noted his talks were treated "as a kind of social entertainment."

The famous Dutch astronomer, Willem de Sitter, as well as the American team of Robert Millikan, Walter Adams, Richard Chace Tolman and Edwin Hubble, were also in Pasadena at this time, and Californians were interested only in what these masterminds were discovering about the universe. The newspapers, in fact, were printing almost as much science as sports news.

Toward the end of his stay, Einstein made a vitriolic speech about Japan's aggression against China. He wanted to know why western nations did not threaten Japan with economic boycott unless it stopped. "The answer," he said, in a calculated slap at the United States, "is that nations pursue a certain course for their own miserable and temporary advantage and are unwilling to subordinate their selfish aims to the well-being and prosperity of society as a whole."

He cut short his farewell press conference at the ship because the questions were so trivial. One man had asked him if it were true that he had discovered a way to get helium from the sun.

"Aren't you finding it easier to talk to reporters?" asked an earnest man, who misinterpreted Einstein's curtness.

"There is an old German proverb which says that nobody can get used to being hanged," Einstein said.

The sixty-nation disarmament talks in the bleak gray halls of the Peace Building in Geneva foundered within weeks. Nobody could agree.

Einstein saw that his years on the public stage had accomplished nothing. He was bitterly disappointed. The Geneva talks seemed a prelude to war instead of peace. So he decided to intervene once more. He went to Geneva in May, 1932, with the British pacifist, Lord Ponsonby, to focus world attention on the farce. If he could arouse enough public opinion, nations might somehow be forced to resolve their differences concerning disarmament.

Konrad Bercovici, the Romanian gypsy author, was in Geneva to record the drama for the American magazine, the *Pictorial Review:*

"All the newspapermen left the conference chambers when the news spread that Einstein had arrived in Geneva. Even some of the delegates decided that a look at the great man was worth more than listening to bacteriological and aerial discussions.

"He had no official standing at the Peace Conference. He was no delegate of any power. He was not even an accredited newspaperman. And yet no one questioned him when he passed through the gates of the Palace watched over by burly Swiss policemen. No one questioned his right to be there. No one, except a Balkan delegate, disputed his supreme right to be there.

" 'Who sent for him? What does he represent? Whom does that Jew represent?' the Balkan delegate disputed.

"He was hushed down. An American correspondent actually hit the fool in the mouth with the paper pad in his hand.

"It was curious to see the silver-haired, heavy-set man walking up the broad stairs of the Peace Palace, with hundreds of people following him at a respectful distance. Years of interviewing had not given the newspapermen that familiarity with Einstein which they assume even with crowned heads.

"There was no 'Howdy, King.' They all stopped two or three steps below him, ranging themselves quietly when he turned, smiled and said he would talk to them later on.

"A young reporter almost fainted with excitement when Einstein asked him for his lighter to rekindle the cigar he was smoking.

"He walked into the conference room. The technician of the Aerial Committee, reading a paper at that moment, stopped for a moment, then continued. That brief second, however, was an acknowledgment, a more marked acknowledgment of the greatness the man radiated than if everyone had stopped everything they were doing and applauded him. All eyes were turned toward Einstein. Where he was, the world was. There was no denying that. The man has divine charm . . .

"I saw Einstein at the Bregues Hotel several hours after his unexpected appearance at the Peace Conference. His eyes had not lost their angry tinge, and his voice was still high, and he was still puffing hard at a cigar.

"The hotel clerk had told me that Einstein had been playing the violin uninterruptedly until I arrived.

" 'What did he play?' I asked.

"The clerk shrugged his shoulders.

" 'I couldn't make it out. He made his violin do the weirdest things: yell and yowl and screech. I thought at times he was trying to break it. And I heard him curse and fume while he was playing.' "

During his interview with Einstein, Bercovici referred to the disarmament talks as a "comedy of peace." Einstein rebuffed him sharply:

"This is not a comedy. It is a tragedy. The greatest tragedy of modern times, despite the cap and bells and the buffoonery. No one has any right to treat this tragedy lightly and to laugh when one should cry. We should be standing on rooftops, all of us, and denouncing this conference as a travesty . . . Delegates have come here under the guise of peace to foster war . . . We are not nearer peace fourteen years after the Armistice of the Great War than we were the day before the Armistice was signed. We have waited long enough for the politicians and the statesmen to accomplish what they have promised to accomplish. Peace. Peace. Eternal peace. We have sent them here to make peace . . . They have cheated us. They have fooled us. Hundreds of millions of people in Europe and in America, billions of people the world over, as well as billions of men and women yet to be born, have been and are being cheated, traded and tricked out of their lives and health and well-being. We have waited long enough. We have had enough patience with their half measures and their promises. Enough. Enough . . ."

Bercovici said Einstein's voice had become almost hysterical.

At his press conference, Einstein was completely subdued. He kept saying that people should take matters into their own hands and send their own delegates to Geneva. A French reporter said Einstein talked only "generalities," then left Geneva abruptly.

Later, Bercovici was dining at the Bregues Hotel. Anatoli Lunacharski, head of the Russian disarmament delegation, came in and Bercovici called him over.

"Did you hear what Einstein said?" asked the author.

"A dreamer, a naive dreamer," said the Russian. "Just because he knows mathematics, he thinks he knows everything. We need practical men—practical men, you understand?"

Einstein was mystified at the silence with which the general public greated the Geneva fiasco. He began to think that people did not really hate war at all. A few League of Nations officials suggested he initiate a public discussion with another great world figure on the cause and cure of war. This might shed more light on the puzzle. Einstein thought it was a great idea. He chose Sigmund Freud. He had many reservations about

Freud's discoveries, but he counted his mind as perhaps the most original in the world.

In his opening letter to Freud, Einstein sought to get to the root of the problem by stages. In the first place, he said, the way to enduring world peace was to set up an international legislative and judicial body to settle all arguments between countries. This meant the nations would have to surrender some of their sovereignty. But there were power-hungry cliques in every country which fiercely rejected this idea. They were ready to go to war to preserve full sovereignty or acquire more. How could these small groups of hotheads coax the masses to fight a war when wholesale suffering and death was inevitable? Obviously, reasoned Einstein, people must have an innate lust for hatred and destruction. And this lust was easily aroused. Therefore, the basic answer to preventing wars must lie in finding a way to control or lessen the destructive instinct.

Freud agreed with Einstein's analysis, but his long letter of reply dug so much deeper into the core of the problem that Einstein was overwhelmed. He read Freud's letter over and over again, muttering to himself: "What a marvelous man."

The Freud document, more than four thousand words long and beautifully written, contained no sure fire solution for ending wars. But his explanation of *why* there was no foreseeable solution fascinated Einstein.

Freud identified two completely opposed kinds of human instinct—love and hate. Man had the instinct to preserve and procreate. Equally, he had the instinct to destroy and kill. "Each of these instincts is every whit as indispensable as its opposite," said Freud. "The phenomena of life derive from their activity, whether they work in concert or in opposition." When a nation was summoned to war, the people responded with their destructive impulses. Ironically, warmongers could stimulate these impulses by appealing to the love instinct. Self-preservation and acquisitiveness, two reasons for war, were both extensions of the love instinct. Because of this interaction of the instincts, there was no likelihood Man could suppress his aggressive tendencies. "War is biologically sound," Freud summed up dryly.

Very subtly then, he worked on a thought that had not occurred to Einstein. Exactly why were he and Einstein pacifists? Pacifism was an idiosyncrasy, not strictly normal. Freud was certain that the reason could be directly attributed to their high degree of cultural development. They had undergone physical changes as well as mental as their cultural development heightened. It was similar to the change in some animals when they became domesticated. It was an organic process, and as it advanced, there was a scaling down of the basic instincts of love and hate. He and Einstein hated war because it was both intellectually and *instinctively* repulsive. This organic change was not altogether good, however. Freud said it impaired the sexual function and tended to turn the aggressive impulse inward instead of outward.

This was the background to Freud's one positive conclusion about war and peace: "Whatever makes for cultural development is working also against war."

In a way, Freud had psychoanalyzed Einstein. He had suggested another reason for his willingness to sacrifice his family for his work and had explained why Einstein had only pangs of sentimentality. The older the physicist grew, the more he lived in his intellect. He was now more obstinate about his scientific convictions, but he was as indecisive as ever about everyday matters that were unimportant to him. The analysis also gave one explanation of why Einstein did not brood and did not build up resentments. He had only flashes of hate or other high emotion. Mostly, he was serene. He was able very quickly to resign himself to personal disappointments, both in physics and in politics.

Some time later, Einstein wrote to his old friend Zangger: "A deepening intellectuality is the single way to fend off this abominable people's world."

During his correspondence with Freud, Einstein was asked to support several pacifist projects. But he was not convinced that any of them would be effective. He hemmed and hawed, and kept in the background.

The leftist French author, Henri Barbusse, was organizing a world anti-war congress for the summer of 1932. He asked Einstein to be a sponsor. Einstein replied that the congress would be a waste of time. Barbusse submitted that men like Upton Sinclair, John Dos Passos, George Bernard Shaw, and H. G. Wells had agreed to act as sponsors. Einstein then wrote back, saying that he would be glad to participate. Soon afterwards Barbusse sent Einstein a public announcement to be signed by the sponsors. It charged that Japan's attack on the Chinese mainland was really aimed at the Soviet Union, a country "dedicated to its great task of socialist and human construction." Einstein refused to sign it. He said Russian leaders aimed at "complete suppression of the individual." Most of the other sponsors also refused to sign.

The exchange between Barbusse and Einstein went on for weeks. When the congress opened in Amsterdam in August, Einstein was listed as a sponsor. He would not attend in person, but he sent a message calling for international justice. Subsequently, he learned that the congress was dominated by members of the Communist Party. He ended up by disassociating himself from it altogether.

This episode was typical of the most frustrating year in Einstein's life. In 1932, he could not be definite about anything.

The American educator, Abraham Flexner, had offered Einstein a position at the proposed new Institute for Advanced Study in Princeton, New Jersey. He said he would be welcome on his own terms. The Institute was planned as a free society of scholars—a school of higher learning, said Flexner, that "need at no time ask of itself what practical importance can be expected of this or that person, this or that subject, this or that investigation." Flexner had conceived the idea after a tour of English and German universities, and two philanthropists, Louis Bamberger and Mrs. Felix Fuld, had donated five million dollars to make the Institute a reality. Flexner first planned a school of mathematics, for which he wanted Einstein as a foundation member; later he hoped to add schools of economics, politics, humanistic studies.

Flexner first approached Einstein at Pasadena in February, made the offer at Oxford in May and came to Caputh for his answer in June.

It was a cold, drizzly day, as Flexner recalled it in his autobiography. He had to wrap up in an overcoat. He was surprised to find Einstein in his summer flannels.

"I dress according to the season," Einstein explained, "not according to the weather. It is summer."

The two men talked all afternoon and half the night. "By then," said Flexner, "it was perfectly clear Einstein would come to the United States."

But the next day he had changed his mind. Elsa Einstein told her friend, the writer Antonina Vallentin, who was visiting at Caputh, that Albert could not face the thought of leaving Germany for good.

In Berlin, Nazi students were demanding that all Jewish students be banned from the university. There were daily beatings on the campus. The Nazis promised not to take any action against Jewish professors—at least, not yet.

Miss Vallentin told Einstein that his life was not safe in Berlin. He did not want to discuss it.

In her biography of Einstein, Miss Vallentin said that she shared a carriage in the train back to Berlin that night with a dozen slightly drunk young men with swastikas in their buttonholes. Their talk was lewd, malicious, anti-Semitic. They said they would like to murder Berlin Police Commissioner Bernhard Weiss, a Jew, and they suggested several obscene methods of dealing with Frau Weiss.

Miss Vallentin telephoned Elsa the following day, telling her to force Einstein to accept the Princeton post. And Einstein agreed, to stop his wife's tears. But a few days later, he said he was staying in Berlin. This irresolution lasted all summer and into the fall. Meanwhile, the Reichstag was being dissolved and reformed, but with little hope of breaking the deadlock between the parties. Nazi Storm Troopers were committing new atrocities every day.

Einstein's son, Hans Albert, paid a vacation visit to Caputh. But Mileva would not come anywhere near Berlin. She was devoting herself completely to Edward. She was resigned to seeing Einstein only rarely now. Since she could never have him back, it was better that way.

Hans Albert could not give his mother an exact report on Einstein's future plans. He had been offered a position in America but so far had changed his mind six times about accepting it. This was a side of the man Mileva knew only too well.

In October, Einstein finally made his announcement: "I have received a leave of absence from the Prussian Academy for five months of the year for five years. Those five months I expect to spend at Princeton. I am not abandoning Germany. My permanent home will still be in Berlin." Einstein added that he was leaving for Pasadena in December. He would return to Europe in March, then go to Princeton the following October.

"Great news," said *The New York Times*. "While Einstein was in California last winter with de Sitter and other compeers, the universe expanded, collapsed or oscillated on the front pages of the Los Angeles papers for weeks."

But Mrs. Randolph Frothingham, president of the Women's Patriot Corporation and prominent citizen of Brookline, Massachusetts, was indignant. Her group protested to the U.S. State

Department that Einstein was "affiliated with more anarchist and Communist groups than Josef Stalin himself." He should be barred from the country.

"They're right, these watchful citizenesses," Einstein announced. "Why open the door to someone who devours hard-boiled capitalists with as much appetite and gusto as the Cretan Minotaur devoured luscious Greek maidens in days gone by . . . And remember that the capitol of mighty Rome was once saved by the cackling of her faithful geese."

Although the State Department denied the request of the Frothingham group, Einstein was asked questions about his political creed when he went to the American Consulate in Berlin to pick up his visa. He refused to answer. He went home in a rage, and he and Elsa decided not to go to America. Early the next day, American consular officials telephoned to say that the questions had been a mistake. His visa was ready.

A few days before he left, Einstein dictated a message for the German League of Human Rights. It was put on a phonograph record. About politics he said: "I admit the ideal of democracy. I reject any form of national socialism." But the Weimar Republic was on its last legs. Aging President von Hindenburg had given up. Hitler and his chieftains plotted on . . .

It was a hectic semester at Pasadena. The Abbé Lemaître was there to detail his theory about how the universe exploded out of one massive, super-radioactive atom. When Lemaître had finished his main lecture, Einstein jumped to his feet and

175

applauded: "This is the most beautiful and satisfactory explanation of creation to which I have ever listened."

However, the two scientists did not agree on everything. Relativity and the expanding universe did not affect Lemaître's Catholicism. And Einstein saw no reason to budge from his pantheism.

"Once you realize that the Bible does not purport to be a textbook of science, the old controversy between religion and science vanishes," said the stoutish young priest. "Look at it the other way. Should a priest reject Relativity because it contains no authoritative exposition on the doctrine of the Trinity?"

Lemaître was convinced that if Relativity was necessary to salvation, it would have been included in the Bible. As it was, St. Paul and Moses had not the slightest notion on Relativity. They were illuminated on the question of salvation, but as ignorant as their own generation on most other things.

Yet Einstein could not concentrate fully on astronomy or religion. He kept watching the newspapers. On January 30, 1933, Adolf Hitler was named Chancellor of Germany. Einstein hoped that he would be thrown out by some miracle. But he hoped in vain.

The Nazis were taking control of Germany and their platform was anti-Jew, anti-intellectual, anti-pacifist, anti-liberal. It was pro-Aryan, pro-the Fatherland. It was the exact opposite to everything that Einstein had championed.

Weeks passed, but he still put off making his plans. He was due to lecture at a seminar at the Prussian Academy at the end of March. He wrote canceling that, but he did not resign.

Then he heard from a friend that Professor Emil Gumbel had fled Germany. And he recalled his warning of almost a year ago: "What shall become of a people who brutally persecute men like Gumbel?"

CHAPTER 10

THE GREAT EXILE

March 10 was an eerie day.

A warm, thick blanket of air bore down on Los Angeles. Cheerful, everyday sounds of buses and newsboys and people walking were muffled. People yawned and blinked to freshen their eyes. Out at Pasadena, Edwin Hubble lectured on the distant nebulae. But it was difficult for anyone to lift his thoughts to the stars. The city was caught in a moist, closed pocket of the universe.

Einstein felt the oppression. He was glad he was leaving the next day, even if it meant public ordeals in Chicago and New York. There was still the boat trip across the Atlantic to enjoy. Across the Atlantic—to where? He liked Switzerland, Belgium and Holland—all small, peaceful, uncomplicated countries. He kept switching from one to the other. Really, there was only one place he wanted to go—Caputh. How hard it was to put Caputh out of his mind, to give up all hope of returning.

Hubble finished his talk and Einstein walked back to his apartment. Elsa was packing.

She looked at her husband's pale, tired face. She guessed what he was thinking. "As long as we are together, Albertle, it does not matter where we go," she said softly.

"I must make a statement soon," he said.

An hour later, Evelyn Seeley of the *New York World-Telegram* knocked at the door. She had come for a cheery farewell interview. She was given a world scoop.

"I am not going home," Einstein told her. "You can say that I am not going home." He said Germany was a "sick" country without freedom, tolerance or equality. He could not bear to live there under such conditions.

Soon after this, Einstein left the apartment. He went out into the sultry afternoon to hear another lecture. Evelyn Seeley stayed on to talk to Elsa. It was feminine chatter about how embarrassed Elsa was every time Albert took off his coat in public and revealed shirt sleeves chopped off at the elbow. Miss Seeley kept thinking of the tragic look on Einstein's face when he said he was not going home. And when she herself was leaving, she saw him walking back across the campus. His head was down. He looked a little shrunken.

She glanced at her watch. Six minutes before six. Suddenly the earth trembled and moaned. In the distance, rolling through the still air, came a sound like drums. Earthquake. Miles away, buildings crumbled and people died. But at Pasadena the earth just shuddered and was quiet again. Miss Seeley looked quickly at Einstein. His pace had not changed. His head was still bowed. He had not even noticed.

Einstein awakened, on his fifty-fourth birthday, on the train to Chicago. A few hours later, in the fog-gloomed Chicago train shed, photographers tried to pose him stepping off the platform.

"Break the rule; smile for us, Professor," they shouted. He did not smile.

He suffered an official luncheon in Chicago. The only pleasant moment was a meeting with Clarence Darrow. Einstein praised Darrow for his eloquent defense of teacher John Scopes in the world-publicized court fight over the Darwinian theory some years earlier.

When Einstein's train stopped at Albany on the way down the Hudson, Dr. Paul Schwarz, New York's fat, popular German Consul, came puffing aboard after an all-night trip by car to corner Einstein in a closed compartment. Schwarz had known him in Berlin. Convinced that the gentle, detached scientist was too naive about politics to realize fully the terror the Nazis were bringing to Berlin, he wanted to make certain that Einstein would not go back. The consul made a blunt plea: "If you go to Germany, Albert, they'll drag you through the streets by the hair." Einstein reassured him, and together they prepared a statement saying the Professor would not set foot on German soil so long as the Nazis were in power. Later, Schwarz was dismissed from his post.

More than three hundred people, half of them newspapermen, were struggling at the platform barrier when Einstein's train pulled into Grand Central. Guards would not let them through.

"But he's my cousin," protested Alice Steinhardt, who actually was his cousin.

"Yeah, that's what they all say," growled a guard.

The Einsteins, escaping the horde in a freight elevator, got into a waiting car at the northern entrance to the station. The windows were rolled up just in time. Einstein looked at the crowd surging forward; his face grimaced under his large black hat.

Sick to death of politics, speech-making and crowds, Albert and Elsa were reluctant guests of honor that night at a banquet held in the Hotel Commodore ballroom by the Friends of the Hebrew University. Presently Einstein broke free from the jostle of businessmen who wanted their picture taken with him and tugged at the sleeve of Harlow Shapley, director of the Harvard Observatory. "I was feeling lonesome before you came," Einstein said, drawing Shapley aside for a talk. "This sort of thing is not for me. I put up with it because it means a lot of money for my charities in Palestine."

At dinner, Congressman Sol Bloom, at the head table next to Einstein, graciously gave up his seat to Shapley. The physicist and the astronomer became absorbed in the universe. Einstein used his squab carcass to illustrate a point—the ribs were the heavens and the backbone the Milky Way. Guests shifted their attention to Elsa. She hated banquets; she had never mastered the art of genteel eating. She realized that while her husband could get away with anything, she was expected to be the perfect guest. Elsa was weak-sighted and on this night she drank from her finger bowl.

Hurriedly the eyes of the guests swiveled back to Albert. He was sketching something for Shapley on the back of a place card. Seconds after he had finished, a man swooped over his shoulder and carried off the card as a souvenir. Einstein looked at him in complete astonishment.

Speeches followed the dinner. Einstein spoke about the new importance of the Hebrew University for Jewish students who were now fleeing persecution in central and eastern Europe. He talked of the colonization work and added that "if the speed of growth does not satisfy some of our hotheaded and impatient brethren, let us remember that in social structures, as well as in organisms, the most worthwhile are not those which grow and mature most rapidly."

He sat down to wild applause. This led to more speeches. But one man, a wizened little eye specialist with a small uptown practice, did not get to make a speech. He had steeled himself all day to make his first public address. He had polished his few words over and over again. But nobody called on shy Max Talmey, Einstein's memorable boyhood friend. Einstein did not even see him.

A group of liberals and pacifists gave Einstein a small reception next day. He said the world should be more aware of the evils of Hitlerism and make sure they did not spread. One newspaperman misinterpreted this to mean that Einstein advocated foreign military intervention in Germany. Berlin newspapers picked up the story and started a series of bitter editorial attacks.

A typical comment was carried by the right-wing *Berliner Lokal-Anzeiger:* "Good news from Einstein—he's not coming back . . . Relativity is in little demand by us now. Quite the contrary. The conceptions of national honor and love of country, which Herr Einstein wanted to abolish, have become absolute values to us. So the outlook for Einstein here is very bad."

Einstein and his wife embarked on the *Belgenland* for Antwerp on March 17. During the crossing, they read snatches of news from Berlin on the ship's bulletin board. The offices of the Zionist Federation of Germany had been searched. Jewish physicians were sacked from hospitals and Jewish judges were thrown off the benches. Berliners were told not to deal with Jewish storekeepers. Hitler was demanding from the Reichstag dictatorial powers for four years. Bruno Walter, the Jewish conductor, canceled his Frankfurt concert and fled to Austria . . .

BERLIN, MARCH 20: German Nazi storm troopers today surrounded the summer house at Caputh of the renowned scientist, Dr. Albert Einstein. They suspected it was being used as an arms cache. After ransacking the house, the soldiers admitted they had found nothing more lethal than a bread knife. Dr. Einstein's sailboat was confiscated.

Einstein read the news with a heavy heart. He had expected some sort of reprisal, but he did not think the Nazis would take his sailboat.

Elsa's only concern was for her two daughters. They were still in Berlin when she had last heard from them. After the *Belgenland* reached Antwerp and she learned that Albert's bank balance and securities in Berlin—some seven thousand dollars worth—had been seized to prevent their use "for treasonable purposes," she was shaking with fear. She managed to get through to their Haberlandstrasse home by telephone. A servant told her tearfully that Margot had started for Paris two days before to join her husband, Dmitri Marianoff. Ilse and her husband had just left for the Dutch frontier. Nothing had happened yet. Still, Elsa did not breathe easily until a few days later when Margot reported from France and Ilse from Holland.

Meanwhile, Albert and Elsa had renounced their German citizenship and taken a small house at the Belgian coastal resort of Le Coq-sur-mer. They were joined there by Helen Dukas and Walter Mayer.

"All I want now is a little peace and quiet," said Einstein. It was an impossible wish.

He wrote a concise letter of resignation to the Prussian Academy. Immediately, the academy board publicly accused him of spreading vicious lies about Germany. It said he was a traitor to the Fatherland because, instead of defending the Hitler regime against "absurd" charges from abroad, he was actually siding with the enemies.

Since his experiences during World War I, Einstein had had no illusions about the character of many German intellectuals. He was hurt, however, when he discovered that Max Planck was among those who welcomed his resignation. It prompted him to make a rare personal defense. He wrote Planck: "Surely there will come a time when decent Germans will be ashamed of the ignominious way in which I have been treated. I cannot help but remind you that, in all these years, I have only enhanced Germany's prestige and never allowed myself to be alienated by the systematic attacks on me in the rightist press, especially those of recent years when no one took the trouble to stand up for me . . ."

The anti-Semitic fury of the Third Reich grew steadily worse during April and May. Hundreds of Jewish scholars were forced to flee the country. At midnight on May 10, students and Nazis crammed Berlin's Opera Square to watch a bonfire made of the books of "decadent" authors like Freud, Thomas and Heinrich Mann, Erich Maria Remarque, Walther Rathenau. Among the ashes next morning was the charred cover of *Relativitätstheorie* by A. Einstein.

Although Jewish businesses were liquidated and Jewish lawyers and doctors barred from practice, thousands of Jews in Germany still hoped that the horror would pass. In any case, many of them did not have money enough to leave the country. Nor did they have anywhere to go. Their strategy was to lie low and wait for the Nazis to forget them. And as they read exaggerated versions of Einstein's attacks on the Hitler dictatorship, many came to believe that the professor was provoking the anti-Semitism. They wrote letters to Le Coq-sur-mer, pleading with him to be silent.

"We get as many angry letters from Jews as we do from Nazis," said Elsa. "The very people who idolized Albert are now calling him mud."

Einstein could only answer that he was following his conscience. "The situation in Germany shows what happens when people do not speak out against evil," he insisted.

And in speaking out himself, he felt he was helping the Jews by arousing world protest against their persecution. He saw proof of this growing contempt for the Nazis in the offers of professorships he received from universities in several countries. Except for a bid from Moscow, he accepted them all to show his appreciation of these anti-Nazi gestures. It did not occur to him that the colleges might be more interested in Einstein, the physicist, than in Einstein, the homeless Jew. And he did not consider, then, how he would divide himself among some six countries.

By the end of May he was hopelessly entangled. He was bound to spend his winters working in Princeton, his summers at the University of Madrid, at least one month each year at Oxford, and he had lecture commitments for Brussels and Leyden. On top of all this, he was offered a chair at the College de France that would occupy much of his time. And again he had signaled his tentative acceptance.

Then Chaim Weizmann announced from Palestine that Einstein need not be "a wanderer among the universities of the world." The great physicist belonged at the Hebrew University with his own people, said Weizmann.

This was too much for Einstein. He had put himself in the painful position of having to choose between many universities and countries. His first commitment was to Princeton. With much apology, he declined all the others.

He did, however, visit Oxford in July to give a series of lectures and to convince notable Britons that there was a grave military menace posed by Germany. Refugees had told him of German factories working night and day to turn out ammunition, guns and tanks. His English host, Commander Oliver Locker-Lampson, introduced Einstein to Winston Churchill, Sir Austen Chamberlain and David Lloyd George. Einstein told them Britain and the rest of Europe should levy a total economic embargo against Germany until armaments production was stopped and Hitler was toppled from dictatorial power.

Of these English leaders Churchill, at least, impressed Einstein. "He is an eminently wise man," he wrote later.

Back at Le Coq, Einstein found that the Belgian police had put a guard around his house. Underground sources in Berlin had informed Brussels that he was marked for assassination. The Nazis had offered a reward of five thousand dollars to his killer.

"Melodramatic nonsense," snorted Einstein. But after that, every visitor was politely searched for concealed weapons. When Einstein and Mayer walked along the beach or sat in the sand to discuss the unified field, two policemen in plainclothes kept watch from behind a sandhill.

Einstein's friends praised his resolute pacifism in the face of the Nazi infamy, his calls for moral and economic censure of Germany, but never for military action. Paul Ehrenfest, his closest friend, cautioned him to "hold the line" and not let his emotions overrule reason.

But as the grim summer of 1933 wore on, the tragedy in Germany became unbearable to him. He was certain that when the Germans were powerful enough they would start their conquests. Pacifist slogans would not stop them. He imagined the Nazi heel crashing down on Belgium. All the horrors of World War I would be repeated and much worse this time. France would be attacked—the Nazis felt they had a score to settle with her. Freedom was in jeopardy in all Europe. Jews were on the brink of the darkest age in their history.

Einstein decided that Germany should be kept confined, its

armies held at the borders, until the eventual collapse of the Nazi rule. A new regime in Berlin could not be any worse.

This was the only hope. It meant the building of powerful defenses in all other European countries. It meant, also, the re-gearing of factories to make armaments and the recruiting of soldiers.

In July, pacifists groups unwittingly gave Einstein his chance to announce his change of heart. Two conscientious objectors had been jailed in Brussels and pacifist leaders in France and Belgium asked Einstein to sign their protest petitions. By letter he carefully explained that, while he still detested militarism, the *special* situation in Europe made military service a duty in democratic countries.

"Were I a Belgian," he said in a letter published in Paris in a pacifist journal, "I should not, in the present circumstances, refuse military service. Rather, I should enter such service cheerfully in the belief that I would thereby be helping to save European civilization."

There was an immediate outcry. "I beg you to reconsider," wrote Lord Ponsonby. "Hitler's methods may be insane and criminal, but I am firmly convinced he is not such a fool as to think he could gain anything for Germany by waging war . . ." Einstein was called an "apostate" in Holland and "puerile" in France.

The most dedicated pacifist in the world, Romain Rolland, now sixty-seven years old and still exiled in Switzerland, re-assessed Einstein as a great scientist and a weak human being. Rolland stated bluntly that the physicist no longer had the courage of his convictions and therefore was an unworthy ally in the fight against war. Einstein, for his part, was having second thoughts about Rolland. This man had complete faith in the power of words. Einstein was convinced words would not stop Hitler.

Einstein had never been more alone. German Jews, politicians, scientists and pacifists all demanded his silence. He was accused of being hysterical about Nazi Germany. When he talked about the inevitable German invasion of Belgium and France, he was either scorned or ignored. He told one interviewer: "It is beyond me why the entire civilized world has failed to join in a united effort to make an end to this modern barbarism. Can it be that the world does not see that Hitler is dragging us into war?"

Another notable German intellectual, Professor Theodor Lessing, was as vociferous as Einstein in damning Hitler. They had worked together for liberal causes in the Twenties and were equally hated by the extreme nationalists. Lessing fled Germany early in the year and was now in exile in Czechoslovakia. On August 31, Nazi agents tracked him down and murdered him.

Elsa Einstein turned white when she heard the news. Certain her husband was next on the list, she implored him to go into hiding far away. Einstein realized his danger for the first time, but he wanted to stay at Le Coq-sur-mer until they left for Princeton. Elsa wept and pleaded. She lay awake at night, her head starting off the pillow at every sound. "Control yourself woman," snapped Einstein. "This is cowardice."

The bodyguards were getting nervous, too. The summer was ending and the coast was becoming deserted. They had to work in shifts; the long, chill nights on the beach were irksome and dangerous. A rifleman could pick them off easily. They told Einstein they could not be responsible for his safety if he stayed.

On September 8 Belgian police announced that Albert Einstein was sailing on a private yacht to South America. It was a red herring. That day he left secretly for England on a yacht dispatched by Locker-Lampson to fetch him. He was landed on the Norfolk coast and driven in a closed car to a log cabin on a remote and wind-swept heath. Despite Einstein's vehement objections, Locker-Lampson installed armed guards on horseback around the property. The idea of having guards did not bother Einstein too much, but his host had insisted they all be girls. "They are less likely to attract attention," Locker-Lampson said.

Somehow the newspapers discovered the hideout and the female guards, much to Einstein's embarrassment, but nobody was allowed close to the cabin. "If anyone tries," warned Locker-Lampson, "my girls will give him a charge of buckshot."

Einstein responded favorably to the isolation and monotony of life in Norfolk. His creative juices started flowing better than they had all year. He tackled his unified field theory, reshaping it from the basic Relativity formula. But his new peace of mind lasted just seventeen days.

On September 27, it was reported from Amsterdam that Professor Paul Ehrenfest had killed his sixteen-year-old son and then committed suicide. Ehrenfest had entered his son's room at a technical college. Soon afterwards two shots were heard. Father and son were found lying on the floor with bullets in their heads. Police believed that the professor had had a fit of mental derangement.

When Ehrenfest died, he took part of Einstein with him. The astute little professor personified the good times in Europe—the sparkling arguments and lessons in Leyden, the Lorentz era, the new adventure in physics. Einstein remembered the scores of mediocre students Ehrenfest had made expert. As a teacher, he was peerless. He could tear the most complex theory to the bone in minutes. That was the tragedy in a way. He was a critic, but not an author. An inferiority complex plagued him all his life, yet his skepticism about new creations remained, and in the end, he had to teach things he did not fully accept. He was past fifty and his mind was set. It resisted revolutionary thoughts. Einstein acutely understood this human problem. Old men lose their flexibility. Ehrenfest's confidence as a teacher must have deserted him. And teaching was his reason for living.

A generation earlier, Ehrenfest had not been allowed to teach at a university in his native Czarist Russia because he was a Jew. Brilliant young Jewish physicists faced exactly the same discrimination in present-day Germany. It was disheartening to shout into the wind. Einstein, too, was losing his self-confidence. He felt he was getting old. Young scientists had joked that the Institute for Advanced Study in Princeton was being established so that old scientists could be respectfully put out to pasture. Like all good jokes, Einstein thought this one contained a pinprick of truth. He himself was almost ready for the pasture.

In early October he was given a last chance to speak out.

A mass meeting was organized in London to raise five million dollars to help German Jewish refugees. Locker-Lampson asked Einstein to address the meeting. The *Daily Mail* attacked the whole idea. It accused Einstein of anti-British statements dating back to 1927 when Einstein was a member of the board of the International League Against Imperialism. Scotland Yard objected because Einstein would be too vulnerable to attack. Through Secret Service agents in Berlin, the Yard confirmed that the Nazis had a price on Einstein's head.

Ten thousand people crowded Albert Hall. Einstein was the drawing card, but it was half-expected he would not turn up. Lord Rutherford walked on to the stage, then Sir James Jeans, Sir Austen Chamberlain, Locker-Lampson. Finally came Einstein himself. The crowd rose as one and the ovation lasted a full minute. It sounded good—ten thousand people who wanted to listen and to help. Einstein, crumpled and portly, moved forward to speak. The audience hushed. His hair was whiter than anyone remembered. He looked very tired. He spoke from notes, his arms hanging at his side.

He said he was speaking to them as a man, a European and a Jew. He said the twin disasters of the depression and fascism had brought Europe to an historic crisis. Man's freedom to grow, to communicate and to worship, his very right to be an individual, was in jeopardy. The growing strength of fascism, communism, militarism and nationalism meant the increasing erosion of personal liberty. Now was the time for people to take a stand, to recognize that an end to freedom was an end to worthwhile life.

"Without this freedom, there would have been no Shakespeare, Goethe, Newton, Faraday, Pasteur or Lister," he said. "There would be no decent homes for the people, no railways or radios, no protection against epidemics, no low-priced books, no culture, no general enjoyment of the arts. There would be no machines to relieve people of the drudgery required to produce the necessities of life. Were it not for these freedoms, most people would lead lives of oppression and slavery as they did under the great ancient despotisms of Asia. Only in a free society can we create the inventions and cultural values which make life worth while to modern man . . ."

After the speech, girls passed up and down the aisles with laundry baskets. The money was still heaping up when Einstein left the hall. He walked away thinking of Locker-Lampson's remark about the real menace of Germany and other totalitarian states: "Never in the history of the world has there been this pogrom of the intellect."

Perhaps people would see this truth soon. In the broad sweep of history Einstein recognized a pattern—progress followed peril. He hoped the pattern would hold true again in Europe. But his own role was finished. He had done all he could. Free Europe was the responsibility of younger men now.

Einstein went from London to Belgium to rejoin his family. A few days later he sailed with his wife, his secretary and his assistant to the United States. Elsa's two daughters stayed in Europe with their husbands. Mileva and his sons were safe in Switzerland. Hans Albert had taken a research job in Zurich.

Albert and Elsa stood at the rail and watched Europe dissolve into the horizon.

"We will come back often," Elsa said, "even some time to

Caputh."

Albert's reply was lost on the wind, but he was thinking he would make a complete break with Europe. There were too many emotional ties. He turned on his heel and went to find Mayer.

CHAPTER 11

THE GREAT STONE FACE

The man who arrived in Princeton on October 17, 1933, and strolled along Nassau Street in the afternoon sun, with smoke billowing from his Sherlock Holmes pipe, was a very subdued version of the high-spirited professor of Berlin—and a different man from the young Relativity genius of Zurich.

Gracie Schwarz, the English wife of the former German Consul in New York, noticed the change when Einstein passed through the city. "It was as if something had deadened in him," she said. "He sat in a chair at our place, twisting his white hair in his fingers and talking dreamily about everything under the sun. He was not laughing any more."

Einstein resigned himself to making his permanent home in Princeton. The Institute set his salary at sixteen thousand dollars a year, which was considerably more than he had asked. He bought a suitably nondescript two-story frame house at 112 Mercer Street. Elsa furnished a study for him upstairs at the back. A nature lover, Elsa had half the wall knocked out to make room for a huge window. It overlooked a garden and put Albert next to the trees. He joked that he didn't really feel inside the house, but he got to like the window very much. His other workroom was more conventional—Room 209 of the Henry Burchard Fine Hall of Mathematics, a large stone building on the main university campus.

Every morning, except Sunday, Einstein left his house around nine o'clock and walked the mile or so to Fine Hall. He discussed the unified field with Walter Mayer until noon and then walked home again. The two men worked apart in the afternoons and evenings and compared notes next morning. Mayer's duties frequently consisted of working through mathematical approaches suggested by Einstein. Mayer was a pure and dedicated mathematician. However, he was getting a little impatient with the unified field and wanted to pursue his own ideas.

People could not resist darting curious glances at Einstein every time he appeared on the street. But they did not bother him for autographs nor ask him to pose for pictures.

Tradesmen found him lovable, polite, serene, kindly, gentle and detached. Colleagues at Fine Hall used exactly the same words to describe Einstein to friends. He was the new "saint" of Princeton. When he patted a little girl on the head, everyone in town grew shiny-eyed.

"Princeton is a wonderful little spot," he wrote to Queen Elizabeth of Belgium, "a quaint and ceremonious village of puny demigods on stilts. Yet, by ignoring certain social conventions, I have been able to create for myself an atmosphere conducive to study and free from distraction. Here the people who compose what is called 'society' enjoy even less freedom than their counterparts in Europe. Yet they seem unaware of this restriction, since their way of life tends to inhibit personality development from childhood."

The American spirit of "rugged individualism" had completely vanished by the 1930's, at least in Einstein's eyes. People had much the same outlook on life, prizing comfort and security above everything else, and the way people raced about, breathlessly trying to match each other's material possessions, struck Einstein as rather ridiculous.

He continued to think of himself as a European, explaining that the European spirit was bound up with originality in personal opinions and actions. Differences in thought and taste were encouraged. "One cannot establish with reason the worth of these values because they are basic principles in the approach to life," said Einstein. "I only know that I affirm them with my whole soul."

Whenever possible, Einstein talked in German. His English was still poor at this time—his vocabulary was little more than five hundred words—but it slowly improved in Princeton, and his accent became less pronounced.

Elizabeth of Belgium asked Einstein when he was going to visit Europe. He replied that so many "obligations" awaited him there that he had not been able "to find the courage for such a project." He had closely followed the calamitous events in Hitler's Germany—Germany's withdrawal from the League of Nations, the new German-Polish entente, the impending collapse of the disarmament talks. As much as he tried to isolate himself from the tragedy, he could not help getting upset. He knew that if he returned to Europe, even for a short visit, he would get entangled in politics.

Physics was his refuge, but he had gone a long time now without the heady joy of success. He was almost alone in his conviction that the popular quantum theory was not an adequate foundation on which to base the future of physics. He was trying to explain everything in nature with a field theory, but more and more he feared that he might never reach a satisfactory conclusion. He had attempted a dozen different mathematical approaches without dramatic progress. He knew what he wanted to do, but the tools—all the mathematical systems extant—were not good enough for the job.

"If only I knew more mathematics," he complained, over and over again. "I'm like a man struggling to climb a mountain without being able to reach its peak."

Walter Mayer did not want to stay on the treadmill with Einstein indefinitely. In 1934 he had his chance to bow out gracefully when a clever young physicist named Nathan Rosen called on them in Room 209. For his master's degree Rosen had written a dissertation based on Einstein's first field theory. Although he had since taken his doctorate in a different branch of physics, he was anxious to discuss his field calculations with Einstein. Rosen came for a visit, but he stayed on for three years as his new assistant.

They wrote several theses together, including a classic critique of quantum mechanics, but the unified field remained just out of reach.

This did not deter Einstein. He locked himself deeper into the problem. Rarely did he show his frustration. Rarely did he show any high emotion. He became a man of eternal outward serenity.

The writer Max Eastman recounted in his book *Great Companions* how he had talked with Einstein in Princeton one day after visiting a large dairy farm where the cows did nothing but eat, sleep, chew and walk a few steps for their twice daily milking. They were the happiest cows he had ever seen. "The comparison seems a little foolish, perhaps, and disrespectful, but . . . Einstein, too, seemed permanently contented and happy."

Einstein withdrew more and more from the people around him. The moral disintegration of Europe pained him, but he told himself the insanity would end one day and a new era of peace and justice would come. This would evolve without his help. No longer did he flash into public affairs with spirited calls for internationalism. He made some statements, but they lacked sting.

"Among my European friends, I am now called *Der grosse Schweiger* [The Great Stone Face], a title I well deserve," said Einstein.

In the spring of 1934, Elsa Einstein's older daughter, Ilse, died and was cremated in Paris. Elsa was inconsolable. She kept her daughter's ashes in the house. Months later, she wrote to a friend: "I never stop longing for her." Then Margot came from Paris to join the family and that helped a little.

Margot was having her own troubles. Since her marriage in 1929, her husband had not been able to keep a regular job. He dabbled in magazine writing, public relations, welfare work. He was not an expert in anything. Einstein had lost patience with him long before. Dmitri Marianoff turned up in Princeton, late in 1934, with a scheme to establish farms for Jewish refugees. The project fell through and Marianoff told Margot he could not support her any more. She started divorce proceedings soon afterward.

In his biography of Einstein—smartly repudiated by Einstein himself, Marianoff accurately revealed one of the physicist's foibles—an aversion to the telling of social white lies.

Just before the separation, he and Einstein went to a private dinner in New York with Henry Morgenthau and other businessmen, apparently in connection with the farm project. Margot had been invited, but she was timid and avoided strangers.

"Where is your wife?" Morgenthau asked Marianoff.

"She is at home with a bad headache," Marianoff replied.

"No, no," Einstein interrupted crossly. "That is not true. The truth is that my daughter is not sick. She is very shy and will not come."

Einstein himself avoided social engagements. Norman Steinhardt Muller, a New York stock broker and a relation of Einstein's, frequently went to the Mercer Street house for Saturday night dinners. Wanting to repay Einstein, he suggested dinner at his club and a movie. "I cannot think of such escapades," Einstein wrote back. The word "escapades" delighted Muller who was at the time a prominent man-about-town. He found Einstein a "funny duckling."

As a matter of fact, an aura of cuteness was developing around Einstein. He did nothing purposely to contribute to the legend. It was not necessary.

Harvard University wanted to confer an honorary degree on him. But it was known that he had enough honorary degrees to paper his house, so Harvard feared he would not come to the ceremony. Harlow Shapley interceded. He wrote to Einstein, inviting him to stay at his house and he added, craftily, that Einstein must bring along his fiddle. The Shapleys enjoyed musical evenings. Einstein immediately accepted. Elsa called Shapley on the quiet and said Albert's stomach was very weak. He had to be served non-caffeine coffee and he must not be offered cigars.

Aware of Einstein's dislike for fuss, Harvard officials kept the news from the press. But inevitably there were rumors. The day before Einstein was due, a secretary in the university office picked up a phone and heard a small, accented voice mutter: "Please, I am here at the station. There is nobody to meet me. What shall I do?" The secretary apologized: "I'm sorry, Professor Einstein. We weren't expecting you until tomorrow." In such fashion did a newspaperman mimic confirm the rumor that Einstein was coming to Harvard.

After dinner the next night, Einstein started fishing for his pipe. He kept his eyes on the cigar box Shapley was handing around. It came within reach. "Ach, my wife," said Einstein. Then he took a cigar.

The string quartet, with Einstein playing first fiddle, was a great success. Later, Shapley asked his guest if he could stay over for another night of music, depending on how he felt after the ceremony. "Oh, that is nothing," said Einstein. "Art is everything. I'd like to stay very much."

Einstein was rarely seen in New York. When he did go to the city, he headed straight for the east side apartment of his friend, Dr. Gustav Bucky, an X-ray specialist and a world leader in medical photography. Bucky had deserted Germany at the rise of Hitler. "One of us had to go," he explained. He was a gently sardonic little man, who could match Einstein point for point in many intellectual discussions. Einstein, however, had a basic knowledge of everything and a deceptively simple way of presenting the meat of an argument that kept him in the lead. Bucky's wife Frida was an expert pianist and a composer. Einstein felt closer to Europe in the Bucky home.

On Christmas Eve, 1934, Einstein left his Manhattan hideaway to see a Broadway movie about international munitions makers—*Dealers in Death*. It was his first and last visit to Broadway.

The newspapers heard about it and sent reporters to the theater before Einstein had even bought his ticket. One cub's assignment was to ask Einstein whether he believed in Santa Claus. When he asked the question, Einstein laughed it off. The reporter chased down the aisle, pleading: "Do you, Professor? Do you?"

Two hours later, Einstein came out and there was the young reporter, still crying, "Do you, Professor?"

"My boy, Santa Claus is a personal thing," said Einstein. "I'll think it over and issue a statement some time."

In Princeton, Elsa and Helen Dukas stood guard over his private life. The only newspaperman who got through was fifteen-year-old Henry Rosso, who wanted a biographical piece for the Princeton High School newspaper. "It is a known fact that I was born," Einstein summarized. "I discovered that nature was constructed in a wonderful way and our task is to find out that mathematical structure of nature."

Ever since Zurich, Einstein had welcomed visits by scientists with genuine problems to discuss. He kept up the custom in Princeton. He also continued to write encouraging notes to bright students who were brought to his notice. Philip H. Phenix, aged nineteen, a mathematical physics major, received one of these notes for a thesis on rotation. Phenix met Einstein briefly in the common room at Fine Hall. The great man seemed very friendly to him, "but not the YMCA type." Phenix later became a professor of education.

Loved for his kindness toward others, Einstein would no longer accept favors for himself. He refused gifts even if they were only pipes or phonograph records. He wanted to be as independent as possible. This showed in his dress. Elsa had managed to keep him fairly neat in Germany, but in Princeton the suits and white shirts went into mothballs. Most days, his attire consisted of a leather jacket, a pair of old trousers that slid below the navel and a pair of soft shoes. When the weather was warm, he changed from the leather jacket to a gray undershirt and from shoes to open-toed sandals. He gave little care to his hair, teeth or fingernails. All this was deliberate sloppiness. He saw that American men dressed this way on weekends when they did not have to conform or put up a front. He decided to do it all the time.

A New Jersey congressman offered to have waived the usual five-year waiting period so that Einstein could become an

American citizen immediately. Einstein said he did not want special treatment. He and his family were still on visitors' visas. They needed permanent resident visas before they could apply for citizenship and begin the five-year wait. Under an old law, these visas had to be obtained outside the country.

In May, 1935, Einstein and his three women—Elsa, Margot and Miss Dukas—sailed for Bermuda.

The Governor invited the Einsteins to dinner the first night, but Albert preferred to go to a little restaurant in Hamilton. The beefy Germany chef heard Einstein was in the place and came out of the kitchen to talk. He had no interest in science, but he knew Einstein was German and he wanted to reminisce about the old country. For a while, Einstein forgot his unified field. He had an uproarious conversation with the chef. The next day the two men went sailing together and stayed out for hours. Einstein's laughter could be heard from the beach.

Summer came early that year. The heat did not bother Einstein, but it seemed to increase Elsa's despondency over Ilse's death. To cheer her up, Einstein rented, for the warm weather, a large house, complete with tennis court and swimming pool, at Old Lyme, Connecticut. He also rented a sailboat and spent most of his time dawdling about the Connecticut River. Whenever he saw a car coming up the driveway, he escaped in the boat.

"He's just like a baby," Elsa apologized to a group of local women who had felt the Einsteins deserved a courtesy call. All they could see of the professor was a broad back disappearing behind a tree.

During his stay in Old Lyme, twenty reporters tried to

interview him. The only one to succeed was Jack Layer, a very persistent photographer. He waited on the doorstep for eight hours, until Einstein took pity on him and agreed to pose. He ended up by rowing Layer about the river in his boat for special candid shots.

Some days later, in a nearby town, a man stopped Einstein in the street and said his face was familiar. Hadn't he seen him somewhere before?

"Quite possibly," said Einstein. "You see, I'm a photographer's model."

When they returned to Princeton, Elsa developed a swelling in one eye. She felt weak and short of breath. Doctors diagnosed an inflammation in the heart. Her condition looked serious.

Einstein did not tell his wife of the diagnosis, but Elsa noticed he was unusually concerned about her.

This new tragedy drove Einstein further into his cocoon. And when General Jan Christiaan Smuts wrote from South Africa asking Einstein to send a message of encouragement to the peace-workers in Europe, he declined. He said his views were already well known.

Leopold Infeld, the Polish physicist who had met Einstein sixteen years before when Infeld was a student in Berlin, came to Princeton on a fellowship and immediately went to see Einstein in his office. He could not take his eyes off Einstein's tired, yellow face.

Without even inquiring after Infeld's health or asking what he had been doing all those years, Einstein went to the blackboard and drew equations to show his present line of work. The

Pole had a quick mind. After studying Einstein's papers for a few days, he pointed out a way to simplify the mathematical structure. By this time, Rosen had left, so Infeld joined Einstein as an assistant.

Infeld had worked before this with Max Born and other great physicists, but he had never known a man like Einstein.

"Other scientists have a switch which allows them to turn off or at least to decelerate the mechanism [of research] by a detective story, exciting parties, sex or a movie," Infeld wrote in his autobiography, *Quest*. "There is no such switch in Einstein's brain. The mechanism is never turned off . . . It seemed that the difference between life and death for Einstein consisted only in the difference between being able and not being able to do physics."

Elsa's condition deteriorated through 1936. By December, she was dying. Einstein spent many hours at her bedside, reading and talking to her. But he had his emotions under firm control. Although there were tears in his eyes, his head was clear. "In this atmosphere of coming death," said Infeld, "Einstein remained serene and worked constantly."

December 21, 1936, started off as quite a warm day. It grew colder after breakfast. By late afternoon it was below freezing. Large flakes of snow were falling in the early evening when Elsa Einstein died.

Shortly after Elsa's death, Einstein asked his son Albert to visit him. He suggested that Albert, who was then working at the hydraulic laboratory at the Zurich Polytechnic, might even find a job in America. Einstein did not say he was lonely.

But Albert knew that he was and came on the next boat.

The man who stood on the pier in New York was a wan replica of the exuberant, devilish father Albert liked to remember.

In the month they spent together at Mercer Street, Albert found that his father had lost nearly all his naturalness. His guard did not relax often, although several times Einstein looked up fondly at his son and talked of the walking tour they had made in South Germany during World War I. "Remember how nice it was?" he would ask.

For a minute then, his eyes shone. His heart was bare. Albert's own reserve slipped away. But he he did not have a chance to respond, for in a flash, Einstein would resume his cautious, smiling serenity.

Albert toured the United States and got himself a research job with the Department of Agriculture in South Carolina. He settled down and brought his wife and children to the States. His father was more pleased than he would ever admit.

But, in the late Thirties, there were dozens of men who counted Einstein as a sort of father. Among these were the Jewish teachers and research scientists driven from eastern and central Europe by the scourge of anti-Semitism. Many appealed to Einstein for help. He wrote countless recommendations to university boards, educational foundations, and special refugee committees . . . "Could you spare a small fellowship for Peter Meyer, a fine chemist? I strongly recommend him" . . . After a while, the committees began to treat Einstein's letters warily. Some of these protégés were no good at all.

Perhaps the best was Valentin Bargmann, a physicist. He was like a young edition of Einstein, outwardly tranquil, with a deep passion for science and music. He had a tremendous respect for Einstein's courage, both in blazing a new trail with Relativity and in doggedly sticking to his conviction about the unified field. Bargmann stood in awe of the older man. But as usually happened, this awe evaporated in the first few minutes of discussion. There was not the slightest shred of pretense about the man. Bargmann had ideas. Einstein was eager to hear them. A personal problem? Perhaps he could help. Einstein wanted to be of service. He got Bargmann a job teaching at Princeton University and later took him on as his assistant.

Infeld, meanwhile, also needed help. In the spring of 1937 his fellowship and his money ran out. Einstein offered him part of his own salary. Infeld refused but suggested they collaborate on a popular book about the development of physics. For Infeld's sake, Einstein agreed.

All that summer and into the fall, Infeld sweated over the book. Einstein made suggestions and checked the manuscript. It was published in 1938 by Simon and Schuster under the title, *The Evolution of Physics*.

With Einstein as one of the authors, it became a best-seller, jumping ahead of *How to Win Friends and Influence People* on the lists. Its success defied all polls telling what readers were supposed to like. Einstein paid no attention to the excitement. He had not even opened the book once it was between covers. Infeld, however, was now solvent and able to go on with his career. That had been Einstein's only aim.

Much later the book was published in Russia, but it did not become a best-seller there. A review in the Soviet magazine *Sovetskaya Kniga* said that "all science is party [i.e. ideological] science."

"Bourgeois scientists are trained in the ideas of idealistic philosophy, and this exerts a direct influence on science as they practice it," continued the review. "An uncritical attitude towards bourgeois scientific literature brings the danger that the alien ideology of 'physical idealism' may penetrate our Soviet physics . . . Soviet scientists must actively develop modern physics on the basis of Marxist dialectic materialism . . . So an analysis of Einstein's and Infeld's book once again confirms Lenin's words that 'once they begin to talk about philosophy, one cannot believe a single word uttered by any of these professors.' "

Then the reviewer added a footnote protesting that the book did not contain the name of a single Russian physicist.

As the year 1938 closed, Einstein himself was more concerned with another of his books—a collection of his writings on liberalism, pacifism, Zionism and science that had been published some years before in Holland. He read his old essays through again, thinking of how much they reflected a better, more hopeful world. For since then, the spirit of freedom in Europe had become so weak that leading statesmen had gathered in Munich to throw a great chunk of democratic Czechoslovakia to Hitler just to curb his appetite for a while.

Sadly, Einstein sat down and wrote this eloquent postscript to history:

"Reading once again the lines I wrote almost ten years ago, I receive two strangely contrasting impressions. What I wrote then still seems essentially as true as ever; yet, it all seems curiously remote and strange. How can that be? Has the world changed so profoundly in ten years, or is it merely that I have grown ten years older, and my eyes see everything in a changed, dimmer light? What are ten years in the history of humanity? Must not all those forces that determine the life of man be regarded as constant compared with such a trifling interval? Is my critical reason so susceptible that the physiological change in my body during those ten years has been able to influence my concept of life so deeply? It seems clear to me that such considerations cannot throw light upon a change in the emotional approach to the general problems of life. Nor may the reasons for this curious change be sought in my own external circumstances; for I know that these have always played a subordinate part in my thoughts and emotions.

"No, something quite different is involved. In these ten years, confidence in the stability—yes, in even the very basis for existence—of human society has largely vanished. One senses not only a threat to Man's cultural heritage, but also that a lower value is placed upon all that one would like to see defended at all costs.

"Conscious man, to be sure, has at all times been keenly aware that life is an adventure, that life must forever be wrested from death. In part the dangers were external: one might fall downstairs and break one's neck, lose one's livelihood without fault, be condemned though innocent, or ruined by calumny. Life in human society meant dangers of all sorts; but these dangers were chaotic in nature, subject to chance. Human society, as a whole, seemed stable. Measured by the ideals of taste and morals it was decidedly imperfect. But, all in all, one felt at home with it . . .

"To be sure, the first World War had already shaken this feeling of security. The sanctity of life vanished and the individual was no longer able to do as he pleased and to go where he liked. The lie was raised to the dignity of a political instrument. The war was, however, widely regarded as an external event. It was thought of as an interruption of man's normal life from the outside, universally considered unfortunate and evil. The feeling of security in regard to human aims and values remained, for the main part, unshaken.

"The subsequent development is sharply marked by political events that are not as far-reaching as the less easily grasped socio-psychological background. First, a brief, promising step forward characterized by the creation of the League of Nations through the grandiose initiative of Wilson. Then the formation of Fascist states, attended by a series of broken pacts and undisguised acts of violence against humanity and against the weaker nations. The system of collective security collapsed like a house of cards. It was a manifestation of weakness of character and lack of responsibility on the part of the leaders in the affected countries, and of short-sighted selfishness in the democracies . . . which prevented any vigorous counterattack.

"Things grew worse than a pessimist of the deepest dye would have dared prophesy. In Europe to the east of the Rhine, free exercise of the intellect exists no longer. The population is terrorized by gangsters who have seized power. Youth is poisoned by systematic lies. The pseudo-success of political adventurers has dazzled the rest of the world; it becomes apparent everywhere that this generation lacks the strength and force which enabled previous generations to win, in painful struggle and at great sacrifice, the political and individual freedom of man . . .

"And yet I know that, all in all, Man changes but little, even though prevailing notions make him appear in a very different light at different times, and even though current trends like the present bring him unimaginable sorrow.

"Nothing of all that will remain but a few pitiful pages in the history books, briefly picturing to the youth of future generations the follies of its ancestors."

CHAPTER 12

URANIUM-235

Niels Bohr, the greatest atomic physicist in the world, arrived in New York on the Swedish liner *Drottningholm* on January 16, 1939. Before he left the boat he was handed a cable from Lise Meitner, a German refugee physicist who was working at Bohr's laboratories in Copenhagen. The cable said: SUCCESS.

Lise Meitner meant she had split a uranium atom into two pieces. The two pieces weighed a fraction less than the original whole. The missing grain had changed to energy and exploded the uranium atom. She measured this release of nuclear energy by using Einstein's equation $E = MC^2$. It was staggering. If she had split enough atoms—all at the same time, she might have flattened the whole of Copenhagen.

Within hours, Bohr was in a car on his way to Princeton. He had intended spending a few months with Einstein, hoping to resolve their differences about quantum physics. But now he had something more urgent to discuss.

Matter is made of atoms. An atom is made of a nucleus carrying a positive electrical charge, and around the nucleus are electrons, all charged negatively. The aggregate charge in the electrons balances the charge in the nucleus. An electron is apparently complete in itself, but a nucleus is made of neutrons and protons. The neutrons have no electrical charge. The protons are positive and therefore determine the total nuclear charge.

Chemical elements differ only in the number of protons in their nuclei. It happens, however, that the number of neutrons in atoms of the same element can vary. This changes the weight, but not the charge. These variations are called isotopes. Uranium, which is very rich in neutrons and therefore one of the heaviest of all elements, has three isotopes. Their numbers are 238, 235 and 234.

In the early Thirties, the Italian physicist, Enrico Fermi, used neutrons like bullets. He got them by mixing radium salt with powdered beryllium. Radium freakishly emits positively charged "alpha particles" as it naturally tears itself to pieces. These particles break up the beryllium nuclei and neutrons are released. Fermi shot neutrons into all sorts of elements to see what would happen. Some atoms of the heavier elements were chipped into atoms of slightly "lighter" elements—iron to manganese, for instance. But when Fermi fired neutrons at uranium, it seemed that a "mystery" element was produced. It could not be identified with any of the elements near uranium on the periodic table.

Towards the end of 1938, at the Kaiser Wilhelm Institute in Berlin, two chemists, Otto Hahn and Fritz Strassman, discovered that the mystery element was actually a mixture of nuclear products. Among them was a barium atom. Since barium is about half the atomic weight of uranium, this meant that the neutrons had split some uranium atoms roughly in half. This was incredible. Other elements had merely undergone transformations. But some uranium atoms were burst asunder.

Hahn immediately sent word to Lise Meitner, his former associate. She had had to leave Berlin six months before because she was a Jew. She was in Stockholm at the time, but she caught the next boat to Copenhagen to tell Bohr. She repeated the experiment and measured the fission, i.e. the energy release—while Bohr was on his way to New York.

Einstein knew about the neutron experiments up to the point of the Hahn-Strassman discovery. Bohr filled him in on the rest while the two men sipped tea in the upstairs room with the big window at Mercer Street. Bohr speculated that if a controlled chain reaction of uranium atom explosions could be set up, physicists might be able to harness atomic energy for industrial use—or to make bombs.

Although skeptical, Einstein saw the possibilities. He took no part in the rush of experiments with uranium at Columbia University where Enrico Fermi was now working, but he followed the results.

It was soon open season on uranium in laboratories all over the world because Hahn and Strassman published the details of their discovery. Only Soviet physicists lagged. For some reason, Lenin had always pointed to the indestructibility of the atom as a support for dialectic materialism.

Scientists found that it was only a tiny part of the uranium that was volatile. This was isotope 235, which made up less than one per cent of bulk uranium. But when a neutron did smash up a Uranium-235 atom, more neutrons were released. Bohr's idea of a chain reaction looked feasible.

The wire services carried the story from Washington on April 29:

"Tempers and temperatures increased visibly today among members of the American Physical Society as they closed their spring meeting with arguments over the probability of some scientists blowing up a sizable portion of the earth with a piece of uranium. The Danish physicist, Niels Bohr, said bombardment of a small amount of the pure isotope 235 of uranium with slow neutron particles would start an atomic explosion sufficiently great to blow up a laboratory and the surrounding country for many miles. But many physicists said it would be difficult, if not impossible, to separate U-235 from the more abundant isotope 238 . . ."

Separation of U-235 from U-238 in bulk had never been tried. It would be difficult and costly. As much as fifty pounds of pure U-235 might be needed in one chunk to give the neutrons time and space to go to work. If the piece was too small or the neutrons traveled too quickly, they might escape into the air without splitting anything. There was danger, too, for the researchers. If they did make their big nugget of U-235, a stray neutron from anywhere might trigger it off. Nobody in the world now doubted that $E = MC^2$ and it had been proved that every pound of U-235 activated could produce an explosion equal to eight thousand tons of TNT.

The whole idea of an atom bomb did not seem very practical after all. Enrico Fermi, acknowledged leader of the research in America, put the facts before the U.S. Navy in the spring of 1939. An atom bomb was a "bare possibility," he said. Navy officials told him to keep them informed.

Leo Szilard, the Hungarian physicist who had once invented a liquid metals pump with Einstein, was also involved in the research at Columbia. He was more hopeful than Fermi, but he, also, failed to arouse interest in Washington.

Meanwhile, New York economist Alexander Sachs, an unofficial adviser to President Roosevelt, was entering the drama. He had heard from scientific friends about the potentials of uranium fission, and when he found an assessment of the research in the spring issue of the magazine *Nature,* he sent the the article to Roosevelt. Sachs felt the same way as Szilard. Both regarded a European war as a certainty and both worried that Nazi scientists might be pushing ahead on some sort of atom bomb project. If Hitler did get atomic explosives, even America would be vulnerable to attack. Sachs and Szilard felt that American research must continue—and the government would have to pay for it.

These two men gave different versions of what happened next. But apparently they met through a mutual friend and agreed that President Roosevelt must be persuaded to act. Szilard prepared a long memorandum. Sachs wrote a covering note, giving the stark details. But they wanted to inject more drama into the appeal, so they decided to get the support of the most magical name in science—Einstein.

It was July and Einstein was vacationing at Peconic, Long Island. Szilard and Eugene Wigner, professor of theoretical physics at Princeton University, drove out to ask Einstein to write a letter to Roosevelt emphasizing the urgency of uranium research. They were unsure of the address and in Peconic they asked the first person they saw where Einstein lived. It was a small boy. Sure, he knew Einstein. He was up on Old Grove Road. Within an hour, Einstein, in rolled-up pants and undershirt, was dictating a short preliminary letter to Wigner. He actually did not want to but, because of the Nazi atom work, he felt he had no choice.

In the letter, Einstein said it was probable that a chain reaction could be achieved in uranium to release atomic energy. However, the possibility of making a bomb this way was less certain. Sachs and Szilard later made Einstein's letter stronger by saying that the chain reaction was "almost certain" and the bomb was "conceivable." Einstein signed the revised letter.

It was up to Sachs then to present the letter to Roosevelt. Success depended on picking the right moment. In August Roosevelt's mind was trained on ways to prevent a war rather than on building new weapons. In September, Germany invaded Poland and Roosevelt faced a neutrality crisis that kept him busy eighteen hours a day.

On October 11, Sachs walked into the President's office to plead the case for Uranium-235. He mentioned Einstein's letter first, then read his own summary. Sachs was inclined to be long-winded and Roosevelt was looking at the clock. Sachs noticed this. He hurried on to read only the first and last paragraphs of Einstein's letter:

"Some recent work by E. Fermi and L. Szilard . . . leads me to expect that the element uranium may be turned into a new and important source of energy in the immediate future. Certain aspects of the situation seem to call for watchfulness and, if necessary, quick action on the part of the Administration . . . [Sachs noted the part about the chain reaction and the bomb] . . . I understand that Germany has actually stopped the sale of uranium from the Czechoslovakian mines which she has taken over. That she should have taken such early action might perhaps be understood on the ground that the son of the German Under-Secretary of State, von Weiszacker, is attached to the Kaiser Wilhelm Institute in Berlin, where some of the American work on uranium is now being repeated."

Roosevelt was impressed but not convinced. He reminded Sachs that the Navy had virtually rejected bids for help from Fermi and Szilard. He did not see how he could go against his service chiefs. Sachs left his portfolio on Roosevelt's desk and asked for another appointment next day. He was invited to breakfast. Einstein's letter had not been decisive after all, so Sachs dreamed up a different approach.

At breakfast Sachs launched into a long story of how Napoleon once scoffed at the idea of the young American inventor, Robert Fulton, to build steamships that would transport French invaders safely and quickly across the channel to England.

Roosevelt eyed the intense, bespectacled economist quizzically for a moment.

"Alex, what you're after is to see that the Nazis don't blow us up," said Roosevelt.

"Precisely," said Sachs.

From and adjoining room, Roosevelt called in General Edwin "Pa" Watson, his military secretary, slapped the sheaf of documents that included Einstein's letter and told him, "This requires action."

That was the beginning of what became the two billion dollar Manhattan Project to make an atom bomb.

In the early months Sachs was dissatisfied with the progress of the first Advisory Committee on Uranium, so he persuaded Einstein to sign two or three more letters to the President urging haste. Sachs said Einstein scribbled his signature without even reading the letters. The physicist did not want to get too involved, and when Roosevelt later asked Einstein to join the committee, he declined.

Except for his first letter, which Roosevelt may never have read, Einstein really did nothing directly to help the project. When the seal of secrecy came down, he lost contact with it altogether. He did not have to be told what was happening. The best nuclear physicists in America started to disappear mysteriously without trace. Even before 1939 was over, an article by a German scientist named Flugge in the freely circulated German magazine *Natural Science* speculated at length about the possibility of an atom bomb. The only question in Einstein's mind was, "Will it work?"

Einstein felt he had done enough with his $E = MC^2$ which first gave men the notion that mass might be turned into scorching energy.

History was to record that Einstein, through his letter, persuaded Roosevelt to go ahead with an atom-bomb project. In truth, Napoleon may have had more to do with this decision than Einstein. But Sachs and Szilard deserve most of the credit—and each has belittled the role of the other ever since.

CHAPTER 13

TO THE VILLAGE SQUARE . . .

One steaming day in mid-summer, 1940, the younger Albert Einstein was driving his father back to Princeton from his home in South Carolina. Even though the windows were down, the inside of the car was like an oven. Einstein wore Roman sandals, a light cotton shirt, and his white sailing pants were rolled up to the knees. But he still sweltered.

Half-way through North Carolina, Albert stopped at a cafe. His father rarely showed himself in public away from Princeton because of the curious stares and the inevitable requests for autographs. This day, however, he wanted to get out of the car and eat some ice cream in the cool of the cafe. He went in timidly and took his seat at the counter with a dozen or so other hot tourists.

"Whad'll it be?" asked the waitress.

"Vanilla ice cream sundae," said Einstein.

She served him without comment. He looked along the counter. The other people were gulping soda and ice cream.

They took no notice of him. A few passed him on the way to the door. They gave him a cursory glance and kept on going. This had not happened in twenty years. He was being treated just like anybody else.

He talked about "that day in North Carolina" for months afterwards, until his son began to wonder whether Einstein might not have been a tiny bit disappointed at his brief anonymity.

It was a small incident but illustrative, in a way, of Einstein's growing conviction that his role as a public figure might well be over.

For one thing, his stomach pains had returned and doctors still could not find out the exact cause. He was so distressed at times that he thought he would die. He had to guard carefully against over-exertion. He was not allowed to smoke. This bothered him most of all. He kept holding a dead pipe in his hand. A visitor would occasionally bring him some tobacco, but then Helen Dukas would hide it. Yet Einstein would somehow track it down, fill his pipe and steal up to his study to smoke it. He was like a small boy who had robbed the cookie jar. Miss Dukas let him get away with it.

His inability to solve the unified field theory also troubled Einstein. He said all his efforts led to the seemingly inescapable conclusion that the universe was being run like a game of chance. Relativity ruled the planets, accurately explaining and predicting their habits. But quantum ruled the atomic world in which there was no sequence of cause and effect and no possibility of predicting the actions of each little atom. Quantum laws were for mobs of atoms. The individual was overlooked. Everything pointed to the finality of quantum mechanics. Einstein admitted this, but he could not accept it as fact. Somewhere he felt there must be a key to the riddle of why the tiniest grain of matter did this or that, but could he find it? Could any human being find it?

Einstein confided these thoughts to his son. When they met, Einstein asked eagerly about new developments in the hydraulic engineering field. Then Albert questioned his father about his own progress.

"Oh well, you know the difficulties," said Einstein. His voice was flat and edged with a hopelessness that Albert found pathetic. Had his father been the type to brood over past failures and future prospects, he might have committed suicide.

Another reason for Einstein's further retreat from the gaze of the world was the war. The fact that there was a war at all convinced him that his influence on the public mind had been negligible. Few had heeded his calls for internationalism in the Twenties. Fewer had taken his warnings about Nazi Germany seriously enough in the Thirties.

In 1940 he had an urge to exhort the United States to throw its full power behind England. He decided he would be wasting his time. Then several intellectual groups approached him for help in preaching for a new and stronger League of Nations. They, however, did not want to join him in an unpopular campaign to push America into the European war.

"Intellectuals are cowards, even more so than most people," he said, in a letter to the Nobel Prize chemist, Harold Urey.

"They have always failed miserably when called on to fight for dangerous convictions."

In his major public statement of this period, made when he took his preliminary examination before becoming an American citizen on October 1, 1940, Einstein alluded to his own feeling of inadequacy in human affairs.

"Anyone who seeks to affect the course of events must have the gift of being able to exert direct influence on men and their activities," he said in a special broadcast from Trenton, New Jersey. "Intellectuals often lack the gift of impressing their audiences. Among the outstanding American statesmen, Woodrow Wilson probably provides the clearest example of an intellectual. Yet not even Wilson seemed to have mastered the art of dealing with men."

By this time, the Institute for Advanced Study had moved its headquarters to Fuld Hall, a new, red brick building in the meadows skirting Princeton. The offices and lecture rooms spread out on both sides of a tall center clock-tower. Einstein's office was on the ground floor. To reinforce his privacy, his room was equipped with double doors, one behind the other. A casual visitor would open the door facing the corridor and think he had stumbled into a broom closet. A knock on the outer door could not be heard inside. The office had a large picture window, a desk and brown leather chairs. Hanging by the blackboard was a printed sign that said ERASE on one side, and DO NOT ERASE on the other side. Einstein had earlier lost some of his better equations to over-industrious cleaning women.

225

Fuld Hall was a place where silent members walked softly, careful not to disturb the thinking of their fellows. At tea time, they gathered in the common room and nibbled cookies, sipped tea and sometimes chatted. All this was done in a hushed atmosphere. Fuld Hall bore little resemblance to a mess tent on Guam.

A sign in the front lobby read: CHILDREN UNDER 10 ARE NOT PERMITTED IN THIS BUILDING.

The old joke haunted the place: They created the Institute for Advanced Study so that elderly scientists can be respectfully put out to pasture.

For Einstein, the needle was stuck. The record of his life played the same theme over and over again.

He worked at Fuld Hall every morning, as he had at Fine Hall. Usually he walked the mile-and-a-half from his home. When his stomach was bad, he went over in a car, then walked home. A retired couple down the street used to watch for him to pass their house at exactly thirteen minutes after one. If he wore his navy blue stocking cap, they knew it must be chilly outside.

His walking companion was Kurt Godel, a Viennese mathematical genius who had joined the Institute soon after Einstein. Godel, a small, shy, ageless man, liked to relax his brain by discussing philosophy—the finer points of Kant, for instance. So along they strolled, patting the heads of a few children on the way and debating whether Kant went too far in his critique of speculative metaphysics.

Einstein spent his afternoons at home reading and writing letters. His pre-war coverage of one hundred letters weekly was down to about fifty, with Helen Dukas selecting those she felt deserved his attention. He dictated the replies. Completely subordinating her life to Einstein's, Miss Dukas was now secretary, housekeeper, nurse and friend.

Once again, Einstein had three women around him. In 1939, his sister Maja had come from Switzerland for a visit; she had not been able to return because of the war. Now that Maja's hair had turned white, too, she looked so much like her brother that Princeton villagers were startled whenever they saw them together. Maja played the piano and joined in the occasional musical evenings at Mercer Street. If there were no guests, Maja and Albert talked about physics or philosophy or music. They also read to each other. Then, for an hour or so before he went to bed at ten o'clock, Einstein worked on his equations.

On the warmer afternoons of spring and fall, Einstein and Maja or Miss Dukas went sailing on Carnegie Lake, the artificial body of water on the university campus. Einstein had picked up second-hand a battered dinghy with a centerboard and a patched sail. He kept this relic in the university boathouse, run by a down-to-earth man named Fred Biallas. Fred, who knew Einstein as well as anybody in Princeton, echoed the town's regard for its famous citizen.

"Just to be with the Professor seemed to help you ease tension," said Fred Biallas, who had many tense moments with the Princeton boat crews. "In other words, I think it would have been impossible to have held a grudge or be riled while talking to him. He was so serene himself that the feeling seemed to pass on to you.

"In 1942, there were two men having a conference with him on our dock. While they were talking a little girl ran over to him. One of the men pushed the child aside. The Professor put his hands up, stopped the conversation, and went over and talked to the child. I believe this was a grave subject about which they were all talking, but he took time out to make the child happy. That was the Professor.

"Another time I was away for a couple of days. In the meantime, the Professor had been down to the boathouse and left a bag for me to pick up when I came back. Now this was just an ordinary brown grocery bag, but in it was a wonderful pipe and tobacco. They were not tied with ribbon as most gifts would be. That was the Professor . . .

"He was a wonderful man and I could go on talking about him indefinitely and all that would be said would be good."

Einstein defied man or nature to stir him out of his placidity. If he was becalmed on the lake, he waited for a breeze to take him to shore. The cab driver ordered for five o'clock would pace the dock impatiently. Einstein would signal him to go away. Even if the breeze took three hours, he waited. He rather liked it. His thinking was particularly sharp in a becalmed boat.

"Hurry and tension and anything infringing on concentration was like a bodily pain to him," said Gustav Bucky, who often spent summers with Einstein at Saranac Lake in upstate New York or out on Long Island. Apparently, all the nonessentials of life hurt Einstein. Every time he rented a boat on vacation he stripped it to wood and canvas.

"Only after a long dispute could I get a cushion to sit on in the bottom of the boat," said Bucky.

Einstein was a dim figure on the public horizon during the war.

In June, 1943, he posed with naval officers in Princeton as the new staff member of the Navy's Ordnance Bureau. The officers said he would be doing "explosives research." Much later Einstein told friends that he did have a contract with the Navy but he had not yet done anything.

The following year, shortly before the Presidential elections, he endorsed the Democratic ticket: "To secure a lasting peace and to protect the future world from recurring aggression will be the paramount and superhumanly difficult task of the years ahead. For this job we need Roosevelt."

When Roosevelt died in April, 1945, Einstein called him "irreplaceable." Of all the contemporary world statesmen, he had genuinely respected only Roosevelt and Gandhi. He regarded these two as true innovators. They had ideas and they worked them through to the limit, just as Einstein did in physics. Gandhi's idea, as Einstein saw it, was to reduce human needs to absolute basics to show that man was not dependent on others. Roosevelt's opposite idea was to show the inter-dependence of man in a country that aspired to ever-growing prosperity. Gandhi, like Einstein, reasoned things out carefully. Roosevelt, also like Einstein, relied a great deal on his intuition. The two statesmen proved the validity of both methods.

Einstein liked new and basic ideas in politics as well as in any other field. He looked for ideas that expressed a general truth and could be developed. While he saw some sense in the formula of Karl Marx, he felt that in Russia it had been applied without imagination and had proven unacceptable in practice. It had sabotaged the most basic human heritage of all—intellectual freedom.

In April, 1945, Einstein was formally retired from the Institute for Advanced Study. He was just sixty-six, although he felt closer to seventy-six. The retirement did not make the slightest difference to his routine. He continued to go to his office at the Institute every morning and work there until lunch time. The office with the double door was to be his until death.

He was at his Saranac Lake cottage at eleven o'clock on the morning of August 7, 1945, when the White House announced that an American warplane had dropped an atom bomb on Hiroshima. Helen Dukas heard the news on the radio and went outside to tell Einstein.

"Oh, weh!" he cried.

Since the defeat of Germany and the subsequent reports that Nazi scientists had not pushed ahead very far with Uranium-235 research, Einstein had regretted his letter to Roosevelt. He felt that the world was not ready for an atom bomb. He said it would be like putting a razor in the hands of a three-year-old child.

Einstein knew his physicist friends must have made some astounding progress in the atom bomb project. Leo Szilard had come to him in March, 1945, and asked for a letter of introduction to President Roosevelt. Szilard did not mention his work, he just said he had "great concern for the future" and asked for the letter. Einstein knew Szilard felt keenly about his dual responsibility as a scientist and a citizen. His work must have developed something—something urgent enough for him to want to bother a sick and exhausted President.

Actually, Szilard was already worrying about the post-war armaments race with Russia. Inevitably Russia would make atom bombs. He wanted the United States to initiate studies on international control, with Russia taking part. Despite his letter from Einstein, Szilard did not get to see Roosevelt.

Many other scientists on the project were conscience-stricken, particularly when representatives of fifty nations gathered in San Francisco in April, 1945, to work out a governing charter for the United Nations. Led by James Franck, a German refugee and a pioneer in atomic physics, these scientists drafted an appeal to the Administration:

"We read and hear about all the efforts which the best statesmen devote to peace-planning in San Francisco and we hear about plans to control industries in the aggressor states, but we know in our hearts that all these plans are obsolete because the future war has an entirely different and a thousand times more sinister aspect than the war which is fought now. How is it possible that the statesmen are not informed that the aspect of the world and its future is entirely changed by the knowledge that atomic energy can be tapped, and how is it possible that those men who know these facts are prevented from informing the statesmen about the situation?"

When this appeal brought no result, Franck followed it up by pleading that the first bomb should be exploded in some wasteland. Enemy and Allied leaders alike should be invited to witness the explosion and thus see the folly of continuing this war or ever starting another one. This idea, which Einstein later said he would have supported, was also turned down. Most of the scientists, in fact, said the bomb should be used on Japan to end the war quickly. President Truman agreed . . .

After the bombs were dropped on Hiroshima and Nagasaki and Japan surrendered, Einstein was inundated with requests from organizations of scientists, pacifists, intellectuals, sociologists to join campaigns. All were concerned in one way or another with the atom bomb. Some wanted it outlawed. Some wanted the formula deposited with the Security Council of the United Nations. Robert Hutchins, Chancellor of the University of Chicago, wanted Einstein to attend a conference of scientists to discuss the social problems connected with living with the bomb. The physicist, Daniel Posin, who was organizing a congress on the same theme, said it was Einstein's duty to come and tell the world about the need to put the atomic bomb under international control and for the United States and Russia to shed all military secrecy.

All this was an old story to Einstein and entirely predictable. Internationalizing the bomb was a popular cause. Every intellectual in the country seemed to be for it. But all they did, in Einstein's view, was to talk generalities with great passion and bore the public.

Einstein's own idea closely followed that put forward by the economist-writer Emery Reves in his 1945 book, *The*

232

Anatomy of Peace. Einstein and Reves said the only way to peace was to constitute a world government, a United States of the World, and this must be done quickly. It was a big idea— too big for most of the intellectuals.

In an article in the November, 1945, issue of *Atlantic Monthly* which was widely re-printed, Einstein said the United States, Britain and Russia should draft a constitution for a world government, adopt it, commit all their combined military might to upholding that constitution, and then issue invitations to the smaller nations of the world. This government should have the power to interfere in any country—he named Spain and Argentina specifically—where a minority ruled a majority. Critics pointed out that a minority ruled a majority in the Soviet Union, one of the suggested charter members of the government. Einstein said he was aware of this, but held out the hope that a better balance might evolve. In any case, he was convinced that a world federation was the surest guarantee of peace in the atomic age, and he would stick by this conviction at all costs.

Now back in the public eye again, Einstein kept talking while people were still willing to listen. He struggled into a dinner jacket in December, 1945, and went to a Nobel anniversary dinner at the Hotel Astor.

"Alfred Nobel invented the most powerful explosive ever known up to his time," Einstein said in his speech. "In order to atone for this, in order to relieve his conscience, he instituted his awards for the promotion of peace.

"Today, the physicists who participated in forging the most formidable and dangerous weapon of all times are harassed

233

by an equal feeling of responsibility. And we cannot desist from warning and warning again, we cannot and should not slacken in our efforts to make the nations of the world aware of the unspeakable disaster they are certain to provoke unless they change their attitude toward each other and toward the task of shaping the future . . ."

Many of the physicists Einstein mentioned decided that the public must be educated on the entire atomic issue so that it would understand the urgency of heading off a world arms race. These men felt—and Einstein agreed—that Truman did not have enough foresight to prevent America's professional army men, conservative politicians and "certain industrialists" from turning the war-time alliance between the United States and Russia into a cold war.

The physicists then conceived the idea of an Emergency Committee of Atomic Scientists to raise money for their unique education program. Hans Bethe, Edward Condon, Leo Szilard, Linus Pauling and Harold Urey were original members. Einstein was appointed chairman.

In the ensuing years, Einstein campaigned strenuously for this committee. The publicity given its releases did make the ideals of the physicists well known and, Einstein felt, the committee had some indirect influence in Washington. The committee's most famous pamphlet, called *Only Then Shall We Find Courage,* was based on a long interview Einstein granted *The New York Times* in 1946.

Discussing how the United States should face its responsibilities in a world shadowed by the atom bomb, Einstein said in conclusion: "America's decision will not be made over a table in the United Nations. Our representatives in New York, in Paris, or in Moscow, depend ultimately on decisions made in the village square. To the village square we must carry the facts of atomic energy. From there must come America's voice . . . Science has brought forth this danger, but the real problem is in the minds and hearts of men. We will not change the hearts of other men by mechanisms, but by changing our hearts and speaking bravely. We must be generous in giving to the world the knowledge we have of the forces of nature, after establishing safeguards against abuse. We must not be merely willing, but actively eager to submit ourselves to the binding authority necessary for world security. When we are clear in heart and mind—only then shall we find courage to surmount the fear which haunts the world."

It became obvious to Einstein that his statements were having little effect on the public, no matter how much they were publicized. America seemed resigned to future atomic danger. The United States submitted to the United Nations a plan for supra-national control of atomic energy. Russia rejected it. Einstein believed that to show her good faith, the United States should have voluntarily outlawed the bomb before tabling the control proposal. By failing to do so, she laid herself wide open to charges that she was intimidating Russia to accept American terms unconditionally. Einstein realized, however, that the Soviet Union resisted submission to a world authority on any level.

In October, 1947, in an "open letter" to the United Nations, Einstein stated bluntly that the UN should regard itself merely as a transitional system toward the "establishment of a supra-national authority vested with sufficient legislative and executive powers to keep the peace." Members should start founding the world government immediately, even if Russia refused to co-operate. Delegates to the government should be elected by free ballot among the people of the various nations.

Four leading members of the Soviet Academy of Sciences —Sergei Vavilov, A. N. Frumkin, A. F. Joffe, and A. N. Semyonov—retaliated with an open letter of their own, published in the Moscow magazine *New Times*.

They said Einstein was unwittingly playing into the hands of western "capitalist monopolies," who now controlled their home governments and were anxious to oppress and bleed dry the rest of the world through such a scheme as that suggested by Einstein. They said the United States would have a "regular voting machine" in any world government just as it did at the UN, because most nations were dependent on the United States and had to adapt their foreign policy to the demands of Washington. Einstein's suggestion about free balloting to choose world parliamentarians was ridiculed. Even in the United States, they said, the democratic process was so limp that Negroes were not allowed to vote. A world government would "further the unbridled expansion of American imperialism." Russia had fought hard to become a "really free and independent state." It did not intend to sacrifice any of its gains.

In his reply, Einstein said it was true that in all branches of American public life the influence of the economic oligarchy was very powerful. But he cited Roosevelt's four-time election to the White House as proof that the Russians overestimated the power. Einstein then said that the Russians attacked anarchy in the economic sphere but supported it in the field of international politics by insisting on unlimited sovereignty. Einstein said that the only vital world issue was to deny countries the right to pursue objectives through the use of force. For this, there had to be a world government setting the laws and enforcing them.

Now, Einstein's name surged in and out of the newspapers. People saw him as a doughty old warrior in a do-or-die attempt to stop the cold war and promote his world government. Letters and statements tumbled out of his Mercer Street study. Einstein, the theoretical physicist, dissolved into Einstein, the saintly world citizen—a kind old man devoting his last years to bringing happiness to the earth.

That was the image Einstein put forward to the world. A few newspapers sent reporters to Princeton to help build it up. Friends and neighbors praised his humility and serenity, his many kind deeds. The sweet stories were printed around the world. The myth was the man.

But a very good reporter, Allan Keller, of the *New York World-Telegram,* wrote the facts: "Very few persons in Princeton know him well. They collect little stories and anecdotes about him, trying to piece them together to form a whole, and never getting anywhere . . . Taciturn to the point of fanaticism, the greatest scientist of our time, and one of the four or five greatest of all ages, is still an enigma in his adopted home town. In truth, Einstein the man is as unknown as Einstein the philosopher and scientist."

Behind the enigma was a man still locked in complex mathematical problems that both charmed and enslaved him. He wrote political statements, made broadcasts, addressed rallies by telephone. But he did not attend any of the meetings unless they happened to be in Princeton.

"I cannot tear myself away from my work," he wrote to a close friend. "It has me inexorably in its clutches."

Once, in the middle of calculations, Ernst Straus, Einstein's young mathematical assistant at this time, mentioned the Emergency Committee of Atomic Scientists.

Einstein sighed. "Yes, one must divide his time between politics and equations. But our equations are much more important to me."

In the search for a unified field theory, he had conceived a fantastic new idea: to discard the principle of "no action at a distance"—in other words, to assume that a physical event may directly affect faraway events as well as just its immediate surroundings in space and time.

At first, he was certain that he was on the right track. Then he was not so sure. He told Straus that his ideas were still good and came just as frequently as ever. But age had lessened his ability to pick the best ideas from the rest.

He appeared quite gay and serene, attributes he readily explained by his conviction that he was working on something of utmost and eternal importance.

However, he did not readily share with friends his consuming worry that he would die soon and before he could develop his unified field theory as far as humanly possible. Associates marveled at how he could reject an idea on which he had been working for months, even years, and start off on a new concept without a sign of disappointment. Einstein did not have time for regrets. He was a man in a hurry.

In 1947 he had grown very weak and his intestinal pains were acute. After long consultations, his doctors concluded that he was suffering from malnutrition. Years on special diets to ease supposed stomach ulcers had almost killed him. More nutritious food and plenty of it was prescribed.

Einstein for years had questioned proven formulae in physics, and spent much time trying to work out alternatives. Against this background, the dogmatism he found in the politics of both East and West seemed so petty that he had to take care to curb his public statements.

He summed up his feelings, however, in a letter to an old pacifist friend, Otto Lehmann-Russbuldt: "Things are going much as they did after 1918, except that there are different actors on the stage. They play as badly as they did then, but the general bankruptcy which threatens will be incomparably worse. Having lost the illusion of free will, one cannot even react in anger."

He attended a conference of atom scientists in Princeton called to discuss the next step in the campaign to make sure atom bombs would never again be used as weapons. For his own amusement, Einstein scribbled a "resolution" on a scrap of paper:

"We American scientists, after three days of careful consideration, have come to the following conclusions: We do not know—what to believe, what to wish for, what to say, and, what to do.

239

"On the basis of an open letter signed by Russian scientists, we may construct a parallel resolution for them: After careful consideration, and due consultation with our government, we do not know—what not to believe, what not to wish for, what not to say, and, what not to do."

Einstein, however, was careful not to say anything publicly that would add to the general American bitterness toward the Soviet Union. In fact, he emphasized that Americans did not properly understand the historic problems that had gone into the welding of the Soviet personality. America's postwar militarism was as much to blame for the cold war as Russia's stubborn belligerency, he insisted.

Many people who read his remarks considered Einstein a "pinko." But in private, he often referred to the Soviet Union sarcastically as "Holy Russia." Then, in 1948, he was particularly intrigued when the Central Committee of the Communist Party officially condemned, as anti-Marxist, the rules of genetics. They had been formulated a century before by the Austrian monk, Gregor Mendel. Einstein had studied Mendel's work thoroughly; he thought it magnificent.

1948 was also the year the Leftist movement started to back Henry A. Wallace, a fierce critic of Truman's foreign policy, as a candidate for President. Wallace was leader of the new Progressive Party. He hoped to get Einstein's support, because, when he attacked Truman in 1946, the physicist had sent him a letter praising his "courageous" action. On the publication in 1948 of Wallace's book, *Toward World Peace,* Einstein had publicly linked him with Roosevelt and Willkie as a man of vision.

Now, however, as the Wallace-for-President movement gathered force, Einstein confided to Straus: "I'll have to support him. What a pity he's such an idiot."

Hans Albert Einstein thought his father kept this exceedingly frank side to his personality too much undercover. In fact, Einstein was losing his vitality. The old "hammy" part of his nature was all but gone. The gaiety and mischievousness that delighted his Princeton friends only faintly echoed the Einstein of Switzerland. His emotions were so subdued that Ernst Straus thought the word "sadness" was most inappropriate in describing Einstein.

Yet the aging physicist could still feel personal loss deeply. In 1947 he was saddened when his old friend Paul Langevin, the French scientist, died. Langevin was the last of his European compatriots. "The sorrow brought on by his passing has been particularly poignant," said Einstein, "because it has given me a feeling of being left utterly alone and desolate."

In 1948, Mileva Einstein died in Zurich. Einstein had never discussed his first wife, even with his closest friends. She was a part of his life that he had kept for himself. So his thoughts, as he sat alone in his study with that grim cable from Zurich in his hand, will never be known. Over the years young Albert had become convinced that he knew his father's main reason for breaking with the family. The constant presence of Mileva and the boys would have hindered his work. Mileva and Albert had had their clashes, but their older son felt they had always loved one another. Mileva herself had remained silent about her former husband, his weaknesses and his strength. She had never remarried. And she had always kept that letter Albert

241

wrote in 1919, the one with the bitter-sweet line: "You will see that I will always remain true to you, in my way."

Einstein arranged for Edward to live in a Swiss sanitarium that was run more like a private hotel, where he was free to come and go as he pleased. The father knew he would never see Edward again; he could only make sure Teddy had the best possible attention.

Soon after Mileva's death, Einstein's sister Maja died. She had been bed ridden since 1946, and so that he might stay close to her side, Einstein had given up his summer jaunts to Saranac Lake. He spent hours reading to her, even after she lapsed into a coma. She could not respond in any way, but Einstein felt she might still hear him.

Death now came close to Einstein himself. In December, 1948, his abdominal pains were unbearable. It was more than thirty years since he had first consulted doctors about them. His physicians had stopped his smoking, had virtually stopped his eating, and had warned him not to tire himself. But they had not cured him.

Dr. Rudolph Ehrmann, an old crony from Berlin, and what Einstein called "an imposing council of doctor friends," now diagnosed an intestinal cyst. It would have to be removed. Just before Christmas, Dr. Rudolf Nissen, a former professor of surgery in Berlin, operated on Einstein in the Jewish Hospital in Brooklyn. Nissen actually found several intestinal growths to remove. He also discovered that Einstein's liver was too small; that it was not functioning properly.

Einstein convalesced in Florida—he considered this a criminal luxury—and was back at work in Princeton before spring. A diet of non-fat, well-cooked foods and liver-extract pills relieved his old distress. This enforced rest, early in 1949, seemed to revitalize Einstein's brain as well as his body.

For then, he successfully completed a problem that had occupied him off and on since 1927. This was a very technical exercise. He sought to deduce the law of motion of material particles directly from his equations for the gravitational field. He did this and, roughly speaking, bridged a gap between field and "mechanical" concepts.

His major puzzle remained. He still hoped to combine the gravitational and electromagnetic fields into one structure that would both explain quantum mechanics and delve deeper into the heart of the atom, revealing all its secrets. Einstein went at this with new gusto in 1949. By the end of the year he was convinced that he had found a much better unified field than any of his previous ones. But again it was pure theory; there was no way to test its validity. It did not lead all the way to quantum. For this he blamed both his "stupidity" and the shortcomings of mathematics.

The Princeton University Press published the new theory in February, 1950. It took fourteen pages to cover Einstein's twenty-eight meticulously turned mathematical formulae. Most physicists sighed and said poor Einstein was wasting his time trying to base all physics on the field concept.

The lay public, however, applauded the man who was trying to give greater coherence to the world. This was the Einstein they liked.

Humorist Robert M. Yoder best described this strange

public excitement about the latest abstruse product of Einstein's brain. Writing in the *Saturday Evening Post* for February 25, 1950, Yoder said: "Word that the professor has now carried Relativity further, aroused in this Einstein fan very much the feeling a dog must have when a shiny truck comes down the street. He knows he can't stop it, he can't conquer those twinkling wheels, but as a dog of spirit he certainly is going to run alongside and bark . . ."

CHAPTER 14

DEATH AND THE RIVER

On the night of February 12, 1950, Mrs. Eleanor Roosevelt sat in the Colonial Room of the Park Sheraton Hotel in New York, pouring tea for atomic experts Senator Brian McMahon, David Lilienthal, J. Robert Oppenheimer and Hans Bethe.

A television audience of perhaps ten million people watched and listened as they talked about President Truman's decision to make a hydrogen bomb. Russia had exploded its first atom bomb four months earlier. Truman wanted to make sure the United States kept ahead.

But this was not an easy decision for the scientists assigned to the project. They had to live with their consciences. During the atom bomb development, they had reminded themselves that the Nazis, bent on world destruction, might also be making a bomb. In any case, the bomb was a temporary by-product of atomic energy which would be a great step forward in civilization. But there was no possible way to use the volcanic heat-energy generated in the H-bomb process—except for a bomb. Scientists were being asked to devote their creative talents to the making of a weapon that would kill thousands of families like their own in a few minutes.

Eleanor Roosevelt introduced her special guest star with a slight apology. Albert Einstein could not come to the Colonial Room, so the cameras would go to him. Einstein appeared on the screen, sitting at his Mercer Street desk, wearing an old sweater.

His words that night were his swan song for the human race. It made the front pages of one hundred newspapers. Einstein knew he would never again have the chance to address so many people. He spoke his mind frankly. The last part of his five-minute talk concerned a world government. It was the first part that made the headlines. He was saying that America's entire post-war policy had been based on keeping world military superiority . . .

"How should we act in order to achieve the utmost superiority over the enemy in the event of war? The answer has been: outside the United States, we must establish military bases at every possible, strategically important point of the globe as well as arm and strengthen economically our potential allies.

"And inside the United States, tremendous financial power is being concentrated in the hands of the military; youth is being militarized; and the loyalty of citizens, particularly civil servants, is carefully supervised by a police force growing more powerful every day. People of independent political thought are harassed. The public is subtly indoctrinated by the radio, the press, the schools. Under the pressure of military secrecy, the range of public information is increasingly restricted.

"The arms race between the United States and the Soviet Union, initiated originally as a preventive measure, assumes hysterical proportions. On both sides, means of mass destruction are being perfected with feverish haste and behind walls of secrecy. And now the public has been advised that the production of the hydrogen bomb is the new goal which will probably be accomplished. An accelerated development toward this end has been solemnly proclaimed by the President. If these efforts should prove successful, radioactive poisoning of the atmosphere and, hence, annihilation of all life on earth will have been brought within the range of what is technically possible. The weird aspect of this development lies in its apparently inexorable character. Each step appears as the inevitable consequence of the one that went before.

"And at the end, looming ever clearer, lies general annihilation."

Einstein had said his piece. He wondered how people would react. Many wrote praising his forthright attack on militarism. Others criticized. But, by and large, the public resigned itself to living with the H-bomb, just as it had with the A-bomb.

Some politicians called him "meddlesome," and one or two said he was fellow-traveling with the Communists. Einstein said he traveled with anyone who was for a world government. Unfortunately, Communist Party members were not.

Most scientists assigned to military work shuffled uncomfortably but stayed put. A few of them banded together in a Society for Social Responsibility in Science. Not knowing exactly what they should do next, they applied to Einstein for a credo. Almost wearily he told them what he thought everyone should regard as self-evident. If they were asked to do something evil—like make an H-bomb—and their consciences rebelled, they should refuse to do it. They should refuse even if the government ordered them to do it. Einstein deftly pointed out that the judgments at the Nuremberg trials proved that a man was still expected to follow his own conscience, no matter what his government or general said.

Einstein was pretty sure the Society for Social Responsibility in Science would accomplish nothing of consequence. His own Emergency Committee of Atomic Scientists fizzled out as well. When it came down to tough, unpopular, even dangerous decisions, most intellectuals stammered and stammered but finally compromised. Einstein had found this to be a rule of society ever since members of the Prussian Academy of Sciences had fallen into military step during World War I.

So now, in a letter to Elizabeth of Belgium, Einstein said he felt almost like a stranger in the world. And to another correspondent, he wrote: "It is strange to be known so universally and yet to be so lonely."

He was past seventy, a man with few close friends. His relentless study of the sciences, philosophy, the arts—and his habit of dissecting every piece of information for the basic thought behind it—had put him on an intellectual plateau all by himself. Yet the more he learned, the more he became aware of the "shabbiness" of Man's knowledge.

Physicists visited him only occasionally now. They explained he was "working in a different field." Einstein himself thought they were prejudiced against his particular work.

248

Physics was getting pedantic, he said. Yet it was actually a very primitive science. The atom was the embryo of the universe; it held the secret of the universe. Scientists had split it, but they knew nothing about its inner workings. Sometimes he looked at his basic equations with a strong intuitive feeling that he was on the verge of unlocking the atom. But there were no mathematics to take him further. This was maddening because he knew he was right as far as he had gone.

Next to his work, the various "causes" were secondary. In any event, Einstein said he was a little tired of "dispensing my blessings." Helen Dukas and an economics professor, Otto Nathan, a long-time friend, edited his mail. They answered his telephone and met callers at the door. Margot Einstein still lived at 112 Mercer Street, but she was virtually a recluse.

Music remained Einstein's absorbing interest away from his work. Age had sapped the strength from his fingers; he could no longer play the violin. He improvised more often on the piano and listened to classical radio programs from New York. His standards were exacting. He would wince and mutter "no, no," when a pianist lost the purity of Mozart.

Einstein worked alone now, so music was the only way to get close to him. That was how Manfred Clynes "reached" Einstein.

Clynes was a twenty-six-year-old Viennese-born Australian concert pianist. He came to Princeton from Melbourne in September, 1952, to study music on a Fulbright scholarship. He had two reasons to see Einstein—a mutual German friend had given him an eight-verse poem to deliver to the great man, and Clynes' mother wanted an expert opinion on her thesis outlining an unique approach to atomic weights.

Clynes delivered the poem with a covering note to Einstein's house at night. Helen Dukas answered the door. They discussed the mutual friend for a few minutes. Then Clynes went away.

He was more determined a few days later. Taking his mother's thesis to the Institute for Advanced Study, he asked the receptionist if he could show it to Einstein personally. Within a minute, he was walking into Einstein's office. In an interview with the author of this book, Clynes talked of that first meeting and the friendship that followed:

"Einstein was sitting at his desk. The sun was shining on his face and his mass of white hair. He looked angelic. I was surprised at the smoothness of his face. All the pictures I had seen of him had shown it deeply lined. The pictures did not do him justice.

"He said he had remembered my name from Helen Dukas's message. He asked about his friend and my mission in Princeton. After he had spoken a few sentences, I had the distinct impression I had known him for years. He had a spontaneous warmth and depth and kindness. I had experienced this before with other truly great men. I felt completely at ease and eager to talk.

"I handed him my mother's book and explained the contents. He handed it back when I had finished. 'It is so different from the approach that I have followed for years that it would be better for you to show it to a younger man,' he said. There was no faked interest. This was his opinion.

"I wanted to get Einstein's reaction to my way of looking

at life. I had thought a lot about religion and found the two basic concepts in the idea of God—the Creator and the Being available to each one of us. I felt strongly that the cultivation of the second aspect was one of the main aims of life. This was the essence of mysticism, the transcending of the individual self. It was like opening a window of one's self and letting God in. Of course, with a man like Einstein, I did not have to build up to my point. I told him quite simply, 'The important thing in life to me is to see the holiness in everything.'

" 'I have never obtained any ethical values from my scientific work,' he said. He must have assumed that I saw holiness in *my* work—music. He was right . . .

"A day or two after this, Helen Dukas called to invite me to supper. I remember how bare the rooms looked, few rugs and little furniture. Einstein himself was rather jovial. Over the meal of meat and vegetables and for two hours afterwards, we talked about music. He told me it was as important for him to improvise on the piano as it was for him to work on his physics. 'It is a way for me to be independent of people,' he said. 'And this is highly necessary in the kind of society in which we live.'

"Einstein had discerning tastes in music that went right back to the Renaissance. He had a tremendous love for Mozart but said he also enjoyed the small pieces of Schubert and Schumann. Among the operas, he mentioned only *Boris Godunov* and *Fidelio*. I knew why. Both have sociological themes of freedom. I turned the conversation to Beethoven's last works. Einstein said they tended to be too rhapsodic. They

251

did not have the Grecian beauty of Mozart. I found myself disagreeing, almost violently. 'The music is highly organized,' I said. 'Let me show you.'

"We went down the hall to a music room and Einstein indicated a fine Bechstein which had been given to him many years previously. He said he had had it specially tuned for the occasion.

"First, I played him Mozart's B flat sonata, K.570. His reaction was pure ecstasy. He threw up his arms and cried, 'You are a blesséd artist.'

"Then I played him Beethoven's Opus 111. There is a transfiguring joy inherent in this music. I felt it as I played. This, for me, was a mystical experience. Beethoven himself had said, 'Whoever understands my music is saved.' I had been intuitively drawn to his music since boyhood, long before I read this seemingly pretentious statement. Now I wanted Einstein to share the joy with me.

"I finished and turned to Einstein. He was smiling. He had enjoyed it. But he had not experienced the holiness in the music . . .

"Walking home that night I thought of the connection between Einstein's theories in physics and Mozart's music. Mozart combined formal beauty, grace, *eternity,* in his music. It was, in essence, truly independent of time and place and society. It was the music for Einstein.

"I saw him often during that winter. My early impression of him as a man who felt himself the complete master of his fate and soul deepened. His convictions were unshakable. Hoyle was visiting Princeton at the time and there was excitement over his new theory of creation. I mentioned it to Einstein and he passed it off as 'romantic speculation.' So I asked him why his own latest unified field theory could not be classed also as 'romantic speculation.' He said, 'The difference is that mine is based on a unifying logic and a harmony of thought.' Was it any more final than his earlier versions? 'I can recognize the true Jacob when he comes along,' he said. 'Either this is it, or a completely different approach is necessary.'

"Einstein liked to joke about his fame. I was one of a group of people at his house one night when he talked about the letters he received. He played the jocular host. The people treated him with deference and none seemed close to him.

"A Jewish student had written saying how much he admired Einstein and how he had put the great man's picture on the bedroom wall. 'I'm being considered as a Jewish saint,' quipped Einstein. Another man had asked if he believed in Hell. 'I wrote back and told him that since he had asked about it, he surely would know more about it than I would.'

"We discussed the psychology of music. It reminded Einstein of another anecdote. He told about the time he was a young professor in Prague. Apparently, the emperor came to the university one day and stood on a balcony that happened to overlook the grounds of a mental home. A group of the inmates saw him and started singing, 'God save our emperor.' One of the aides on the balcony looked stricken. 'God save your majesty,' he cried. 'The *lunatics* are singing "God save your majesty." ' Einstein roared with laughter at the memory.

"His best humor carried a touch of satire. In a political discussion, he summed up the history of the democratic process, 'The only progress made in democracy since Athens has been the establishment of Her Majesty's loyal opposition in England.'

"In the spring of 1953, I was to go on an extended concert tour of Europe. Before I left, I wanted to give Margot some Beethoven records. She had often shared our musical evenings and greatly enjoyed Beethoven. There was a record player in the house, but the collection of records was very small. I told Einstein of my intention. 'No, no,' he said. 'I cannot allow it.' His tone was so firm that I said nothing more about it. His desire for independence obviously went to the extreme of not accepting favors from anyone.

"I called at Einstein's house to say good-by. As I was leaving, Miss Dukas handed me a letter from Einstein, suggesting it might help my tour. It was nice to have a personal memento from the greatest living genius, but I did not realize the magnificence of his gesture until I read his words, written neatly in German:

" 'Dear Mr. Clynes: I am highly grateful to you for the great pleasure which your piano playing has given me. In your playing there is combined a clear insight into the inner structure of the work with a rare immediacy and spontaneity of interpretation . . . The technique never supplants the artistic content as unfortunately in our time so often is the case. I am convinced that you will find the recognition . . . to which your achievement entitles you. With friendly greetings, Yours, A. Einstein.' "

In November, 1952, Einstein was offered the presidency of Israel. Chaim Weizmann had just died. In a way, the offer embarrassed the physicist.

The Nazi mass murder of Jews during the war had brought Einstein closer to his race than ever before. He said his heart "bled" for the lost millions. He had been so stunned by the stories of the massacres that he could hardly bear to hear the name—Germany—mentioned. He did not blame just the Nazi soldiers. He blamed the Germans en masse and he never forgave them.

The eventual realization of Israel made him very happy. At least one good thing had happened in the cockeyed world. He felt that if he belonged in any one place on earth, he belonged in Israel.

But he had to decline the presidency. He could not interrupt his last vain effort to get his field theory closer to the atom any more than he could interrupt his breathing. As a president, he would have to move his household, set up another, attend ceremonies, make speeches, greet important visitors, make clever talk. He appreciated the gesture, but he suspected it had originated with someone who did not understand the first thing about him.

Officially he declined because "I lack the natural aptitude and experience to deal properly with people and to exercise official functions."

In a statement to a Tel Aviv newspaper, he said another reason he declined was because of "the difficult situation that would arise if the government or parliament made decisions which might create a conflict with my conscience."

Many in Israel thought Einstein's remark about his conscience was offered more as an excuse than a sound reason. However, there was a basis of truth in what he said.

Einstein was acutely sensitive about a man's responsibility to be honest to himself at that time because of the great Washington "inquisition" in progress under the rough direction of Senator Joseph McCarthy. The Senator had a philosophy: "Scratch an intellectual and you'll find a Communist." He was out to expose every Communist in the country by quizzing a long parade of intellectuals before his senatorial committee.

Inevitably, the intellectuals asked Einstein what they should do.

His answer was published in *The New York Times* of June 12, 1953:

"The problem with which the intellectuals of this country are confronted is very serious. Reactionary politicians have managed to instill suspicion of all intellectual efforts into the public by dangling before their eyes a danger from without. Having succeeded so far, they are now proceeding to suppress the freedom of teaching and to deprive of their positions all those who do not prove submissive—i.e. to starve them out.

"What should the intellectuals do against this evil? Frankly, I can only see the revolutionary way of non-co-operation in the Gandhian sense. Every intellectual who is called before one of the committees ought to refuse to testify—i.e., he must be prepared for jail and economic ruin, in short, for the sacrifice of his personal welfare in the interest of the cultural welfare of his country.

"If enough people are ready to take this grave step, they will be successful. If not, then the intellectuals of this country deserve nothing better than the slavery which is intended for them."

Actually, Einstein regarded McCarthyism as a grotesque joke, but he decided to take the grimly serious approach. His statement did renew the storm of controversy about McCarthyism and most people came to Einstein's first conclusion. It was a grotesque joke. Very few intellectuals had a chance to prove their worth to Einstein before McCarthy was censured.

Einstein rather enjoyed his reputation as an *enfant terrible* in politics and was delighted with an award presented to him, in 1953, by the New York department store Lord and Taylor for "constructive non-conformist thinking." The donors referred to Relativity.

"It gives me great pleasure, indeed, to see the stubbornness of an incorrigible nonconformist warmly acclaimed," he said in his letter of acceptance. "To be sure, we are here concerned with nonconformism in a remote field of endeavor; it is a field which no senatorial committee has yet felt impelled to tackle."

The aging rebel continued to break from his work every now and again to duck in and out of politics. Yet he was more certain than ever that he was going to die within months. In the fall of 1954, his legs were so weak that he found it difficult to walk home from the institute. Frequently he gasped for breath. Doctors diagnosed anemia. They put him to bed, pepped him up with cortisone and had him back at the institute in three weeks. He did not feel at all cured.

In a note to Fred Biallas, his old friend at the Princeton boathouse, Einstein said: "I have given up my boat. It shows signs of decay—like myself."

The boat, by then, was so dilapidated that nobody wanted to take it out on the water.

Einstein's only regret about dying was that his work was incomplete. He had been denied a definitive result to thirty years of brain-wracking toil. His other affairs were in order. With Otto Nathan's help, he had figured out his assets. His will bequeathed twenty thousand dollars and the house to Margot; twenty thousand dollars and his personal effects to Helen Dukas; fifteen thousand dollars to his son Edward; and ten thousand dollars to Hans Albert, then a professor of hydraulic engineering at the University of California. Nathan and Miss Dukas were to serve as joint trustees of his estate.

Hans Albert had rather off-hand instructions from his father about the disposal of his body. It was to be cremated.

"And I don't want the ashes buried," said Einstein. "I don't want people pointing to a hole in the ground and saying, 'There he is.' Get rid of the ashes!"

Medical research scientists had expressed interest in examining Einstein's brain after his death in the hope of finding the seed of genius. Albert asked his father if he was agreeable.

"They won't find anything unusual," said Einstein. "But since it won't make any difference to me, they can take what they want."

Early in 1955, Einstein felt that his brain was faltering. He was uncertain about how to advance in his field theory. He mused about his reputation as a genius and decided it was grossly exaggerated. He attributed his accomplishments in physics to curiosity, concentration, perseverance and "self-criticism." To his way of thinking, his achievements in public affairs were insignificant. For all his dire warnings and appeals to reason, the world seemed hell bent on destroying itself. But he regarded it as his duty to speak out if the cause was sufficiently worthy.

During February and March, even though he was absorbed with his equations, he conducted a long correspondence with the British philosopher Bertrand Russell. They discussed how a select group of eminent men might bring pressure to bear on Washington and the Kremlin to stop the arms race and work toward peaceful co-existence.

Frequently doubled with pain from an inflamed gall bladder, Einstein tried to help mankind to a better world. He and Russell worked out a manifesto. It detailed the inevitable horror of a thermonuclear war and appealed to the governments of the world to acknowledge publicly that war was out of the question. Future disputes must be settled peaceably. The document was mailed to the world's most prominent scientists, both Communist and non-Communist, asking for their signatures. It was then to be sent to Moscow, Peking, London, Paris and Washington. [In July, Russell made public the manifesto, duly signed by many renowned scientists. They still await a resounding response from the governments of East and West.]

Israeli representatives in the United States came to Einstein early in April, asking him to draft a statement for Israeli Independence Day on May 14. He started to compose it on Wednesday, April 13, in spidery handwriting:

"I speak to you today not as an American citizen and not as a Jew, but as a human being who seeks with the greatest seriousness to look at things objectively. What I seek to accomplish is simply to serve with my feeble capacity truth and justice at the risk of pleasing no one . . ."

He wrote of the conflict between Israel and Egypt, and of the larger division of the world into two hostile camps. He wrote at the desk in his study by the light from the big window. Outside, the trees were green once again with the spring . . .

". . . The development of atomic power has imbued the struggle with a ghostly character; for both parties know and admit that, should the quarrel deteriorate into actual war, mankind is doomed. Despite this knowledge, statesmen in responsible positions on both sides continue to employ the well-known technique of seeking to intimidate and demoralize the opponent by marshaling superior military strength. They do so even though such a policy entails the risk of war and doom. Not one statesman in a position of responsibility has dared to pursue the only course that holds out any promise of peace, the course of supra-national security, since for a statesman to follow such a course would be tantamount to political suicide. Political passions, once they have been fanned into flame, exact their victims . . ."

There was a violent surge in Einstein's abdomen. The fountain pen slipped from his fingers. He was sweating. His mouth was juicy. He swallowed. Then he went stumbling down the hall to vomit.

He collapsed that night, and two days later he was admitted to Princeton Hospital. Helen Dukas called Hans Albert from California and Otto Nathan and Gustav Bucky from New York. Two local physicians, Dr. Thomas Harvey and Dr. Guy Dean, were at his bedside. They suspected internal bleeding and suggested that an operation might help. Einstein declined. For half his life, doctors had not been able to get to the root of his internal complaints. It was too late now for any more tries.

On Sunday, April 17, he felt much better and asked for his equations and his unfinished statement for the Israelis. He picked up his equations first.

"If only I had more mathematics," he complained to his son.

Bucky was with him early that night and when he got up to leave, Einstein asked where he was going.

"You should sleep," said Bucky.

"Your presence won't stop me from going to sleep," Einstein grinned.

At about one fifteen that night, April 18, 1955, Einstein muttered something in his sleep. His nurse thought he might need something. She went into the hall for a minute to see if there was a doctor about. When she returned to his bedside, Einstein was dead.

Family and friends hurried to the hospital. But it was not until eight o'clock the next morning that the news was released to the world by the hospital's public relations man, Dan Coyle. Dr. Harvey announced that Einstein's earlier nausea was due to an inflamed gall bladder and that death had been caused

261

by a blister on Einstein's aorta, his main body artery. It finally blew out, said Dr. Harvey, like a worn inner tube. Dr. Harvey also anounced that Einstein's brain had been removed and placed in solution. Nothing could be said about it for some time—until after intensive examination. [Dr. Harvey was still looking at it and probing it—or rather small remnants of it —seven years later. All he would say was that the original weighed two and sixty-four hundredths pounds, apparently a normal weight.]

Eulogies from scientists and statesmen poured into Princeton from all over the world. "All Israel bows its head," said Abba Eban, the Israeli Ambassador to the United States. "His death will be deeply regretted by the German people," said West German Chancellor Konrad Adenauer.

Even as quiet voices on the radio and black headlines in the newspapers hushed the world, the body of Albert Einstein was being taken to a crematorium in Trenton, New Jersey, where at four-thirty in the afternoon, the body was incinerated.

Otto Nathan, the mild little professor of economics, took charge of the casket of ashes. Get rid of them, Einstein had said. Nathan reverently held the last earthly remains of Einstein in his hands. His friend would want it done simply, bravely, and without ceremony.

Nathan drove to a nearby river and dropped in the ashes. A splash, a few bubbles—and Einstein was gone.

INDEX

INDEX

INDEX

Dirac, Paul, 135
Dukas, Helen, 130, 149-150, 184, 202, 204, 223, 227, 230, 249-251, 258, 261
Dyson, Sir Frank, 11

Eastman, Max, 199
Eban, Abba, 262
Ebert, Friedrich, 85, 111
Eddington, Arthur, 9-10, 13, 92-93, 155
Ehrenfest, Paul, 10, 58, 65, 71, 80, 85, 89, 125, 135, 149, 187, 190-191
Ehrenhaft, Felix, 95
Ehrmann, Rudolph, 242
Einstein, Albert, anti-Semitism, 86 ff., 173, 185; atom bomb, 218 ff., 230, 232 ff., 246 ff.; birth, 21; boyhood, 23 ff.; doctor of philosophy, 44; Geneva disarmament talks, 156, 164 ff.; League of Nations, 121, 125, 129, 143, 146; marriages, 42, 79; Nobel Prize, 118, 122; pacifist, 143, 151-152, 159-160, 170 ff., 187-188; Pasadena studies, 149, 154 ff., 163-164, 175 ff.; patent officer, 42-43; professorships—Zurich, 51-53, 58-61, Prague, 54-58, Prussian Academy of Sciences, 62 ff., Princeton, 195 ff.; public lec-

turer, 95 ff., 104, 114, 162; religion, 27, 87, 139 ff., 176; sailing, 137, 144, 227-228; sickness, 71-72, 129 ff., 223, 239, 242-243, 257 ff.; "Ten Fateful Years" essay, 210 ff.; United Nations, 235-236; university student, 33 ff.; Zionism, 87, 97 ff., 120, 143, 145
Einstein, Edward, 50, 59, 62, 123-124, 131, 146-148, 161, 242, 258
Einstein, Elsa, 4, 6, 11-12, 71 ff., 99 ff., 114 ff., 149-150, 161, 173, 179, 181 ff., 189, 193 ff., 204, 206
Einstein, Hans Albert, 44, 59, 62, 67, 70, 79, 91, 123-124, 130-132, 144, 147, 161, 174, 193, 206-207, 222, 241, 258, 261
Einstein, Hermann, 21-22, 26, 30, 32, 41
Einstein, Ilse, 4, 79, 130, 184, 199
Einstein, Jacob, 22-23, 25
Einstein, Maja, 22, 27, 30, 32-33, 60, 227, 242
Einstein, Margot, 4, 79, 93, 130, 183-184, 199-200, 204, 249, 254, 258
Einstein, Mileva, 42 ff., 52, 54, 58 ff., 67, 71-73, 79, 91, 122 ff., 131, 147, 161, 193, 241
Einstein, Pauline, 21-22, 60, 88
Einstein, Rudolph, 71